THE
NEW WORLD-ORDER

THE UNITY SERIES. IX

THE
NEW WORLD-ORDER

ESSAYS ARRANGED AND EDITED

BY

F. S. MARVIN

'*The old order changeth, yielding place to new.*'
TENNYSON

'*L'homme sait le divers et veut l'identique.*'
ÉMILE MEYERSON

Essay Index Reprint Series

BOOKS FOR LIBRARIES PRESS, INC.
FREEPORT, NEW YORK

First Published 1932
Reprinted 1967

LIBRARY OF CONGRESS CATALOG CARD NUMBER:
67-30221

PRINTED IN THE UNITED STATES OF AMERICA

PREFACE

THIS book is based on lectures delivered at two Unity History Schools, one at Danzig in 1929, the other at Stockholm in 1931. The subject under discussion on both occasions was much the same, the history of the world since the War, with special stress on the growth of world co-operation. The bulk of the chapters belong rather to the later occasion, that on biology being the only one printed substantially as it was delivered in 1929. Various circumstances prevented the inclusion of much that was prepared for the Danzig gathering, though the friendly meeting there with large numbers of Poles and Germans and the eager audiences of German scholars under Dr. Bechler's guidance will long remain a pleasant memory in the minds of the English who then visited that fascinating spot.

At Stockholm in August 1931 a similar gathering took place, this time with the co-operation of many Swedish friends and a sprinkling of visitors from Norway and elsewhere. The Swedish authorities entered fully into the spirit of the thing, and assisted the conference in every possible way. Only the recent death of Archbishop Söderblom, one of the greatest international figures in Scandinavia, cast a shadow over the great enjoyment and instruction received by all who took part in the expedition. The contact with Sweden was profitable from every point of view. The work of Swedish men of science finds frequent reference in the chapters on physics and astronomy, while the conference had the advantage of the personal presence of many other Swedes distinguished in various lines of life and thought. Two of these appear in these pages; one, the creator of the most beautiful and famous of modern buildings, the Town Hall of Stockholm, which he is too modest to mention in his chapter on Swedish architecture; the other, the late Foreign Minister of Sweden,

whose stalwart work at the League of Nations has often
won the plaudits of England and other nations at Geneva,
and who now presides over the leading university of his
own country at Upsala. In the case of Mr. Ragnar Östberg,
it was thought fitting, in spite of his own silence on the
subject, to include two characteristic views of his wonderful creation which illustrates so well the spirit of modern
Swedish architecture of which he speaks.

This is not the place to speak in detail of the many lessons
in modern civilization which the visitors in August were
privileged to learn. But it is not too much to say that they
came away with the impression that Sweden is in the front
rank of democratic nations, using in a humane and tolerant
spirit the resources of modern science for the general good.
They felt too that nowhere else could a better centre have
been found for the discussion and dissemination of sound
views on international questions.

The book which follows is framed on lines common to
all the volumes in the Unity Series. Any attempt to make
it exhaustive would have been doomed to failure; the
multiplicity of details would have obliterated the clear
impression of many salient points. What these appear to
him to be the editor has indicated in his introductory
chapter. It so happens that scientific discoveries in the
post-War period provide several turning-points of first-
rate importance. These therefore are treated in the next
two succeeding chapters, but the other side is then suggested, and some balance of interest is offered by two
chapters on typical artistic developments in the same
period, that of literature in England and of architecture in
Sweden. Neither is specially germane to the international
problem, but each is highly characteristic of its own nation
and provocative of questions to others.

After a chapter on biology, which has now become the
central subject in modern knowledge, the book returns to
the general practical topics of education, the contact of

races and the world-treatment of industry and finance,
which are the most urgent problems of the day. For these
the scope of the League of Nations is indicated by
Dr. Undén.

F. S. M.

CONTENTS

I

THE CHIEF NEW THING

By F. S. MARVIN

HISTORICAL parallels are a fascinating game, and one such was being played with vigour a few months since at a meeting in London. A very clever man was drawing parallels between contemporary events and similar events in the past, and suggesting throughout that we might expect similar sequels in the future. Thus, as the Hellenic states at the centre exhausted themselves by internecine war and fell at last under the sway of the greater outside Power, which then was Rome, so, in our own day, the European Powers, having exhausted themselves in the great internal struggle of the War, were falling under the domination of the new outside Power, which now is the United States. And just as, soon after in the Ancient World, a new religion blew in from the East, viz. Christianity, so we might expect, in the decadence of Christianity, another Eastern blast, which this time, he feared, would be communism from the steppes of Russia. It was an exciting picture and plausible, though not attractive, for the prospects held out in every case were of the worst. The chairman, an older and more cautious man, in opening the subsequent discussion, began by saying that he thought there was now a League of Nations in the world and that this might vitiate the historical parallels. The one word was sufficient. These airy structures yield at once to a solid fact of which we can say with certainty that it existed on one side of the suggested parallel and not on the other.

It is because the League is such a fact that we are able to take it as the starting-point in these studies and speak of a new order in the world. Something of a world-wide order has been set up, by the general consent of mankind,

and is in active work, of which it is impossible to say that
any parallel existed before. Aspirations, no doubt, there
have been, and very limited anticipations. They have been
studied in many writings, among them an earlier volume
in this series.[1] But all these earlier efforts fall so far short
of the reality of the League of Nations that we are fully
justified in speaking of it as a new thing in history, in the
same sense that biologists, after discussing the nature and
origin of variations in animal generation, have had recourse
to the idea of a larger change which has been called a
'mutation' and may be the cause, or at least the symbol,
of a new species.

In this book we are treating the League rather as a
symbol than as the cause of the new order in the world.
We have no chapter describing the organization or the
work accomplished by the League because an ample literature exists in which this may be found. But the fact and,
still more, the spirit of the League will be found acknow-
ledged on many pages; and even this does not suffice. It
appears to us that the most important fact in the post-
War world, without an appreciation of which it is impossible rightly to estimate contemporary events, is the
emergence in men's consciousness of a sense of the unity
of the world and its inhabitants. This unity is, of course,
no new thing. But, owing to the acceleration of the process
of mechanical unification in the nineteenth century, and
the shock to the movement given by the War, men woke
up, in 1920 and after, to realize, as they had never done
before, how much they were bound up together, and to
take steps to make this implicit union conscious and effective. This is the chief new thing in the post-War world,
and it is recognized by every serious thinker and by every
one who seeks to act either in the economic, political, or
intellectual sphere.

[1] *The Evolution of World Peace*, Unity Series, IV (Oxford
University Press).

The League then, though the chief political fact since the War, should be regarded as a part only of a great movement and set of organizations all having as their purpose to implement this new consciousness of world-unity. That it is new and dominant would be easy to prove by a comparison of almost any speech or writing on general topics with a corresponding utterance from before the War. We are suffering just now from commercial depression and a fall in prices. Every one who discusses remedies, recognizes that it is a world problem and desires concerted action. In politics, whereas thirty years ago to 'think imperially' was the proud motto of a great party, to-day the only difference in international affairs between our parties is the shade of enthusiasm and confidence with which they regard the League. All wish it to succeed, and all avoid with anxious care the dangers of aggression or secret dealings for selfish ends. We English are no *preux chevaliers* in this matter, for the change of tone is world-wide with inevitable exceptions. Steady efforts are being made everywhere to extend the area of this community spirit and treat those nations who stand outside the League as honestly and amicably as if they were within.

In science the world-spirit is at its maximum and nationalism hardly existent, except where fanned expressly by the orders of a revolutionary government. But even from Moscow, at a recent international congress in London, delegates arrived by aeroplane and begged almost with tears that their long papers be heard. Science is indeed the essentially unifying side of our nature, arising, as it does, from the union of two or more minds and being that aspect of us which, while aware of the diversity of phenomena, *veut toujours l'identique*. But the movement in religion gives confirmatory evidence. In the past it has often tended to violent and internecine difference. So that when we find, as we do, in the same period a growing approximation in religion, we may take it as the strongest possible proof of the reality of a new synthesis. In 1925, six years after the establishment of the League of Nations and the International Labour Office, an international conference on practical Christianity assembled. It was large and representative, practically of all the churches except that of Rome; and Stockholm, where these lectures have been given after another lapse of six years, was the scene.

It is usual in historical surveys to take as landmarks some outstanding dates in the political sphere, and in this case there are three already passed and a fourth now upon us which serve well to divide the time and indicate the march of events. After the formation of the League in 1919 the next great international event was the Washington Naval Conference during the winter of 1921-2. This marked the first step in the limitation of armaments by mutual consent and the union of the three leading naval Powers—Great Britain, the United States, and Japan—for the preservation of peace, especially in the Pacific. Three years later the same method of conference was applied at the most dangerous point in the continent of Europe, and treaties were signed at Locarno which bound France and Germany to respect their mutual frontiers and brought in Great Britain and Italy as guarantors. Germany then joined the League in 1926. Three years later the Pact of Paris, initiated by Mr. Kellogg, the Secretary of State at Washington, brought in the largest possible range of states on a peace basis, including the United States themselves. All the signatories renounced war as an instrument of public policy, and the world is now awaiting the natural corollaries of this declaration. Of these the most important would be a considerable agreed reduction of armed forces, for which a preliminary agreement has been signed and a general conference called for February, 1932.

The details of all these agreements are beyond the scope of this volume, but one or two general facts about them should be noticed which bear strongly on our main thesis. In the first place, they show a widening tendency ; the area covered by the pacifying agreements has so far enlarged that all nations will have met in February 1932 to discuss disarmament. Concurrently with this extension, the League of Nations has been called upon to play a larger part. At Washington in 1921 it hardly appeared ; in 1932 it will be the centre of the action. Lastly, there has been no set-back.

Many people who know all this, and are in principle friendly to the League, are accustomed to allow it to be obscured in their minds by the growth of nationalities and nationalism, which is the other most conspicuous political fact of the period. They speak as if we were in the trough of great waves of national passion which threaten the ship of civilization. It is a curious misconception. In no other way than by an extension of national units was either the League or any effective co-operation between nations possible. The two things are part of the same process, the obverse and reverse of the same medal. All earlier attempts at a League in modern times were doomed to failure just because they had not this basis of free co-operating nations to rest upon. Only from such an organization of suitable units of smaller size could a union of the whole arise, and the evils of which we hear so much— minority grievances, tariff walls, and international jealousies —are the incidental drawbacks. They should be attacked and, as far as possible, remedied, like other complaints of childhood and family life, but the environment in which they arise is not thereby vitiated or to be condemned.

On the contrary the birth of new, and the strengthening of weaker, national units are to be reckoned as—next to world co-operation—the most important achievement of the post-War years. Nationality must rank below the claims of mankind as a whole, but in its immediate effects on individuals it is of greater moment. The post-War years from this point of view present a brighter picture

than any earlier period of history. The figures alone are
eloquent. Whereas before the War there were eight Great
Powers practically directing world-affairs, with sixteen
lesser states occcasionally called into consultation, after
the War the Great Powers are reduced to six, and forty-
seven lesser states take their place in the counsels of
nations, nearly all of them belonging to the League.

These forty-seven minor states spring from the whole
world and not only from Europe, as did the lesser states
in pre-War days. This fact in itself bespeaks the world-
wide character of the new order. We have among the new
members of the world's areopagus not only the Succession
States broken away from the old empires of Germany,
Austria, and Russia, but the members of the British Commonwealth of Nations who now assert their right to speak
for themselves, and another swarm from Central and
Southern America. These are the majority, and to them
are to be added the stray nations of Asia, who are gradually
coming by their own—Persia, 'Iraq, and, one hopes shortly,
Egypt, Syria, and even Palestine. Of Africa as a whole and
its native peoples it will be more convenient to speak in a
later chapter.

But the bald fact that there are now all these new
members of the world's family called in council—whether
in the League or no—conveys but a small part of the
reality of the awakening that has taken place. The world
is actually in face of the most stupendous renascence[1]
which has ever taken place, and its evidence is mainly to
be found in the activities of the smaller nations. Here there
is hope and confidence and intense activity; it is the old
Great Powers who suffer most from depression and unemployment and the 'Untergang des Abendlands'. They too
will recover in their turn, but for the moment the strongest
stimulus comes from the new-born or re-born peoples who

[1] Marquis of Lothian—*Contemporary Review*, September 1931.
General Smuts; Presidential Address to British Association, 1931.

are straining every nerve to make good their heritage. In many cases the older country suffers a temporary loss from the eager competition of a younger rival. It is hard for the Germans of Danzig to see anything but a costly and unnecessary challenge in the building of Gdynia, and British merchants, with their hearts full of imperial unity, find it difficult to swallow the tariffs of Australia and the rest. But we must put, if we can, the question on a higher level, and find a place for all. Each one must make the business arrangements which suit him best, for flourishing neighbours make the best society.

On one matter at least all the new nations speak with a unanimous enthusiasm; they are all devoted to their schools, and proud of them.

It is an easier task, no doubt, for a smaller community to educate itself or make any system of social supervision effective. We shall have to speak more fully about this in a later chapter. But, as a symptom of what is moving in the hearts of these newly-inspired nations, their zeal for education is the most significant. They all show it, and though improvement in education is a general feature of the times, the smaller and the newer nations are most zealous and often most successful. In the new Rumania, for instance, some ten thousand village schools have been built by the peasants themselves on land provided by the landowners. The new Poland has organized a complete system of schools, carefully supervised and manned by a newly-recruited body of teachers, poorly paid but admirable in their devotion. It is more or less the same in every place where a new national movement has come into power. The purpose, of course, is largely national, to strengthen the nation in its newly-found liberty and union. For this reason it is often faced by the obstacles of dissidence in language or religion, or a general reluctance on the part of some minority in the population to identify itself with the aspirations of the nation as a whole. But there is much

more than this involved. These schools are in every case
democratic. The whole people is to be educated. Every
one is to have such training as he is capable of receiving,
and every one in the new polity is to serve the state in the
position he is best able to fill. It is an extension to the
whole world—so far as it is organized on the new national
lines—of those principles which we associate with the
revolution of a hundred and forty years ago in the West,
and which will be easier to carry out in smaller national
units, less subject to the traditions of class and wealth.

This is a considerable item to add to the credit side of
the balance-sheet for the post-War years, and though it
may not seem directly to subserve the interests of international co-operation, yet, in so far as the new citizens
in these smaller states become aware of the general tasks
in which the League and Western civilization are now involved, it will add intelligent force to their support.
And—to return to the League for a moment—it is
not too much to say that, great in the past, the influence of the smaller nations bids fair to be still more
decisive in the future. It is they who have the strongest
interest in preserving the peace of the world and curbing
the armaments of their greater neighbours, and they who
can take the more disinterested view of policy, where large
interests and large populations are concerned. Moreover,
when united, they can make their will prevail.

World co-operation, of which the League of Nations is
the symbol and the chief organ, is the characteristic of the
new age, and we have now seen how its foundations are
laid in the old western states of Europe, with the accession
of a large number of smaller nations, revived, strengthened,
or newly arising, in Europe and without. But the large
omissions will have been observed. Little has been said of
the United States and almost nothing of Russia or China,
her largest neighbour in the East. These, with India, form
the four largest aggregates of men living contiguously

under the same government, and the fact that they have not played a leading part in the story, as we have so far described it, gives rise to serious question. The cases must be dealt with separately. Both India and China are nominally members of the League; the United States and Russia have for different reasons avoided membership from the start. The position of India is due primarily to the fact that she has been and still is under the political tutelage of Great Britain, and in the second place to the fact of her internal disunion. She was, by the action of the then Secretary of State for India, enrolled as an original member on the foundation of the League in 1919. She has continued so to act, hitherto under the direction of Great Britain. At each stage of the League's growth the interest of India has increased, and her membership has become more, though not yet sufficiently, representative of the Indian populations. Her international weight will obviously grow further with the growth of internal unity and nationhood. China, the largest numerical mass of mankind in the world under one government, has not gained so far, compared with India, by her freedom from Western tutelage. Her representative also sits at Geneva, but in view of the disorganization of his country and its want of financial resources, can carry little weight. Her power in the world remains for the future, and at the moment she calls for assistance instead of giving it. America and Russia, on the other hand, are very active factors in world-affairs and, though not in the League, count for more than most of the nations who are. Each of them for different reasons objects to throwing its lot into the common stock. The story of the relations of the United States to the League of Nations is a long and interesting one, far too long for inclusion in this chapter. The sequel only can be given here and the change of heart which it denotes. Having at its inception decided to ignore the League, in spite of the action of her own President in starting it, America has steadily

increased her interest and her co-operation. She takes an
unofficial part in every important piece of international
work, and in many cases things which fall ultimately into
the hands of the League have owed their origin to powerful
initiation in the United States. She is *amicus curiae*, though
not yet sitting in the curule chair. It is anticipated, however, that her formal adherence to the World Court of
International Justice will take effect from the end of this
year.

The case of Russia calls for fuller comment owing to the
fact that, though not enrolled in the League and regarding
it as hostile, she yet stands in the eyes of a large
minority of mankind for an ideal to be worked for. Her
polity, as we saw, has actually appeared to an intelligent
man as a possible religion for the world. Such a state must
contain something worth studying.

From one point of view we may quite truly treat Soviet
Russia of to-day as one of the Succession States, born in
the convulsion of the War and torn away from its old
dependence on an imperialist and autocratic system. This
was its origin, and it shows some of the features which
mark those states. But, whereas the other states had all
national traditions which held them together and which
they wished to revive and extend, in Russia these national
traditions belonged to that very system which the War had
broken and the mass of the people were willing to let fall.
The void was filled by a group of idealists holding a doctrine of social reconstruction drawn from one of the acutest,
but purely abstract, brains of the West. Marx inverted
Hegel, and the inverted Hegelianism was applied with
ruthless vigour to a suffering, dreamy, and unpractical
people who had lost their old masters in the whirlwind.
They had been largely Eastern before, and the shearing off
in the War of their western provinces made them turn still
more to the East. They had been before the War almost
entirely peasants and exporting large quantities of their

produce to western lands. The need of money for the new
régime, and the zeal of their industrial gospel, led the new
masters of the country to industrialize with fury, to regi-
ment the masses in factories and collective farms, partly as
a method of government, still more as a means of flooding
the world with the products of cheap labour and establishing the new régime firmly in power.

Where then is the lure, and how comes it that so many
men, both in Russia and elsewhere, have come to regard
the Soviet experiment as an ideal and their philosophy as a
gospel? Clearly it is the conviction that it is possible for a
small body of men, having seized the helm of State and
possessing certain ideas, so to guide society for millions of
others that all, especially the poorest, will in the end enjoy
the best time earth can give them. It is a belief in the
power of the political machine, used for social ends, which
has given communism its force, a belief not, of course, confined to theoretical communists, but applied by them in a
revolutionary way, without regard to existing traditions
or the hitherto recognized rights of property. At last a
government had come into full power in one of the largest
countries in the world prepared to act on the principle that,
'La propriété c'est le vol'.

We cannot argue here the theoretical point or give the
reasons for a belief that Russian communism is not likely
to become the religion of the world. But, looking for elements of unity in these essays, one is bound to ask what
is here the common ground between what we can trace
progressing in the rest of the world and what is being
pressed with such violence in Russia. It may be found,
we think, in an extract from the Fundamental Statute of
the Russian Universities which lays down that their aim
is 'to direct the whole system of scientific knowledge
towards answering the needs of social reconstruction'.

This is so much the creed of the modern world that it
might easily be thought unnecessary for the Russian, or

any other government, to formulate it. For that reason it is the more useful for us to recall it as a connecting link between them and the nations allied in the League, and to examine its implications before we turn to the differences in application, the absence of other controlling principles, which have in practice led to the breach which actually exists. The Russian formula contains two, or possibly three, very general statements of belief. The first, mentioned last in the extract, is that society needs reconstruction, and to that all thinkers and all nations would give assent, only differing as to the extent and the method of reconstruction. In the sense that it is desirable that social arrangements should be so altered that every one should have a fairer share of good things and be able to enjoy a happier and more civilized life, all would agree; it is the general aspiration and effort of modern societies from long before the War. How to secure this and to what degree the sharing should go, these practical questions at once divide us. When Mr. Bernard Shaw and certain theorists, not now apparently including the directors of Russia, declare for an absolute equality of incomes, most people feel that it is an impossible and not at all an attractive ideal. But such differences should not obscure the fact of a general agreement in aim. The other part of the Russian formula lays stress on the part science has to play in producing this social reconstruction; it is to be supreme. Here the thinkers and still more the practice of the world are at present less decided than on the need for reconstruction. If science in this connexion means the mobilization of every unit in the population to work under directions from above in producing in the least time the utmost return from the soil and other natural resources, then humane common sense would reply that there are higher considerations than the mere productivity of labour. If, however, science is understood to mean the laws of human life as well as those of external natural phenomena, then again the Russian formula would be in keeping with the general educated opinion of the civilized world. More study of the conditions under which the best life may be led and a steadier observance of them are two of the duties most incumbent upon us, and should rank even above those which govern a more productive industry. A science of life, and a science of living together, should take control of the material sciences by which factories are run, and earth, air, and water made to yield their last quota for human consumption.

An analysis of the formula leads inevitably to a criticism of the whole Russian system. Reconstruction directed by science; as the words stand, they might pass for the motto of the modern world. Yet, as we examine them, we come to see how in their application they may cover 'humanity uprooted'. At first it is a difficult puzzle. The very people who might seem to be doing the most urgent work in the world, on the most modern lines, are found to be in violent opposition to the body which stands for world-organization, as well as to the whole past of their own country. Moreover, in carrying out their work, they are inflicting suffering, deprivation, and compulsion on their subjects which no other nation can contemplate without repulsion. How can the paradox be explained, and how does it affect our general thesis that world co-operation is the note of the new order?

Want of complete unity, either in theory or in practice; want also of any sincere attempt to secure it: this is the answer. The Marxian theory fails of comprehensiveness because it isolates the one element of profit-earning labour and elevates it into the one decisive element in social progress. The whole truth is much more complex; all sides of our nature co-operate in determining the form and movement of society, and the most decisive is what we believe about the world and what we desire it to be in relation to ourselves. What changes most in the world, as time goes on, is what man thinks about it, and so far Buckle was right in giving the first place to the intellectual movement. But he was wrong in denying progress on the moral side; our view of human nature and our attitude to other human beings, affected of course by the intellectual change, has also a movement of its own. This in the post-War age has become humane and universal as it never was before. There is no word exactly to describe it, because the thing is new—a feeling of common interest with other men and a conviction that all are partners in a common heritage and travellers to a common goal. Any system or polity which denies or hinders this is out of harmony, not only with the ideal or spirit of the age, but with the structural necessities of society. We must live together to live at all, and what has always been a neighbourly duty, a Stoic maxim, or a Christian command, is now recognized as the most fundamental law of human nature and the condition of all progress in the future.

Science best expresses this because it has sprung from experiences common to all men and been elaborated as an articulate and marvellous system to which all civilizations have contributed. In this, human unity has always been an unquestioned postulate, and nowhere can one find a more serene confidence in the future, a more perfect benignity to the builders of all nations, a more complete indifference to national jealousy than in the great masters of the history of science. Read Tannery or Meyerson, for they lift one into an atmosphere calmer and clearer than even the air of Geneva.

It so happens that this post-War period, which has seen the building up of the League of Nations and the partial appeasement of international wounds, has in the world of science been marked by events as momentous of their kind. Perhaps, indeed, as we now remember 1666 rather as the date of Newton's great law than of our miserable wars with the Dutch, so in a not distant future Relativity and the

new view of the Universe may seem to be more important
than Reparations and the occupation of the Ruhr. In any
case they form a better companion picture to the League
of Nations; they illustrate and do not obstruct the co-
operation of mankind.

BOOKS FOR REFERENCE

Arnold J. Toynbee. *Survey of International Affairs,* especially
    introductory volume on 'The World after the Peace Con-
    ference'. Oxford University Press.
George Sarton. *The History of Science and the New Humanism.*
    Holt & Co., New York.
F. S. Marvin. *The Unity Series* and *The Living Past,* new edition,
    1931. Oxford University Press.

II

THE ATOM

By HERBERT DINGLE

IT has recently been said that the history of science, when contrasted with economic or political history, seems to be distinguished by more definite achievements and a clearer articulation. That is true. An achievement in science remains an achievement, but an achievement in politics or economics as often as not carries within itself the seeds of its own destruction. The partition of the star Sirius, like the fall of Humpty-Dumpty, is irrevocable; the partition of Poland, on the other hand, is a political habit.

The reason for this difference lies in the fact that in science we have achieved a large measure of self-determination, while in politics we are like little children stumbling in the dark with only the rudiments of a blind understanding to guide us. The scientist faces his world and records what he sees. He does not interact with it; he stands outside and brings it within the focus of his observation and intelligence. But the politician does interact with his world. His actions are not self-determined; they are the result of forces which he has not yet learned to understand, and the value of political history lies in the fact that it helps him to interpret them. The history of science is the history of our mastery of the world; the history of politics is the history of our slavery to it.

We might put the matter in another way. Life began in total ignorance, and the subsequent events in their totality are history. The course of history is characterized by a gradual understanding by men of what is happening, and that understanding is science. Science is that part of history which is interpreted, and the ultimate aim of thought is to make all history science.

Now while it is true that science is an understanding of

Nature as a whole, and that the history of science is the history of the growth of that understanding, it does not follow that scientists invariably understand what they are doing. Like other investigators, they use certain means to achieve their ends and, again like other investigators, they do not always find it easy to distinguish the ends from the means. Money is a means of exchanging wealth, but it has become inseparably entangled with wealth itself. Language is a means of expressing ideas, but ideas cannot always be translated; the language is sometimes inextricably interwoven with them. And in the same way, scientific ideas, which are a medium for expressing facts, tend to become confused with the facts they express.

And so it comes about that the history of science has two aspects—an outer and an inner. The outer aspect is the gradual conquest of the mysteries of Nature—the unearthing, observation, elucidation, and ultimate comprehension of the secrets of the world in which we live: the inner aspect is the realization of what we are doing when we achieve this conquest, and of how far we ourselves are unconsciously intruding our own conceptions into the seemingly objective world which we study. The outer aspect presents itself as a continuous process—somewhat kaleidoscopic perhaps, but steadily progressive, never changing form except to move forwards; the inner aspect is that of a set of apparently eternal principles, only once in an epoch becoming disturbed, and then with such cataclysmic violence that those who do not see the continuity of the outer aspect call it a revolution. The period with which we are here concerned has witnessed one of these revolutions, of which the outer aspect also is marked by almost unprecedented activity. Not since the great age of science in the seventeenth century has a development of such significance occurred.

The period in question is characterized by two great landmarks, which every one has heard of under the names of *relativity* and *the quantum theory*. It is true that both these advances of thought were planned in the pre-War period—the beginnings of relativity date from 1905 and those of the quantum theory from 1901—but it was not until the Great War was over that they really became effective.

Early relativity attracted little attention from scientists; it was too suggestive of an unworthy metaphysical escape from an awkward physical situation, and, moreover, it led to no new discovery. It was merely a reinterpretation of known facts, in which, it is true, complexity was dissipated, but only, it seemed, at the cost of common-sense. Not until 1915, when Einstein extended his idea to cover the phenomena of gravitation and thereby automatically removed one of the long outstanding difficulties of Newtonian mechanics, did it seem worthy of the attention of physicists and astronomers. But by that time the world was at war, and the investigation of the laws of Nature was criminal folly in view of the supreme importance of breaking the laws of international relationships. News travelled with difficulty in the scientific world in those days. We in England owe much to Professor W. de Sitter of Leiden, who in 1916 and 1917 communicated to the Royal Astronomical Society a series of papers explaining the new theory and pointing out some of its astronomical implications. Evidently a great new idea had been generated, but an important question remained: Was it true? That question could be answered only by observation of an eclipse of the Sun, and on that observation depended one of the most momentous events in the history of science.

Now eclipses of the sun—blind, unintelligent things as they are—care nothing for the political affairs of men. They occur at their appointed times and places, no matter whether the nations are engaged in tennis tournaments or in a war to end war. And so it was that on May 29, 1919, an eclipse of the sun, almost unbelievably favourable for the crucial observation, was due to occur, not in a region chosen to meet the exigencies of a world at war, but in Brazil and West Africa—places effectively so remote under the conditions of 1917–18 that no hope of taking advantage of the eclipse could reasonably be entertained. Hope, however, is never reasonable, and despite the blackness of the prospect the English astronomers embarked on the long and arduous preparations which the necessary observations would require so that, if it should happen that the war ended in time, the unique opportunity might not be lost. As every one knows, peace came to an exhausted world in November 1918. Two English expeditions were sent out, the eclipse was observed, and the results were reported at a historic meeting of the Royal Society and the Royal Astronomical Society at Burlington House in November 1919. The prediction of the theory had been verified. It was in November 1919 that the theory of relativity took up its place as the supreme generalization of physical science.

We have little time for side-issues, but I cannot refrain from pausing a moment to reflect on the position. In the midst of the greatest war of history, the greatest abstract idea of history came to maturity in a German brain, was ripened and passed over to England by a Dutch thinker, and gave rise to silent preparations which were to lead to its establishment as soon as the strife was over. Members of conflicting and neutral nations engaged in a common task, while over them hung the great shadow of a world war! And of this the world knew nothing until the shadow had passed. There is something ironical in such a situation, but I do not think that the irony is the most fundamental aspect of it.

The quantum theory, as we have seen, was born in 1901, but this also did not take its rightful place in physics until much later. It is concerned with the interaction between matter and light, and in its early forms it emphasized the

characteristics of light more than those of matter—
characteristics which mystified more than they enlightened.
But in 1913 came the development which has led us
directly to the full realization of what the theory means.
In that year Niels Bohr gave, for the first time, an account
of a process by which atoms could emit and absorb light
as they are observed to do. This process could be studied
by means of the *spectra* of bodies—i.e. the kinds of light
they emit when we incite them to radiate—and the period
of physical history from Bohr's paper to the present time
might fairly be called the age of spectra.

I have spoken of 'light', but I should have used the
more general term 'radiation', for our eyes are sensitive
only to a small part of the radiation which bodies dis-
charge, and the spectrum of a body is the analysis of the
total radiation. This includes infra-red and ultra-violet
rays and X-rays as well as light, and if we had restricted
our studies to the visible radiation we should know very
much less than we do about the atoms of matter. No one
can mention X-rays without thinking of the man who,
perhaps above all others, has made exact measurement of
these mysterious radiations possible and brought them into
line with visible light as a means of exploring the atom;
I mean Professor Siegbahn of Upsala. Through him, and
others who have worked in more familiar fields of research,
the quantum theory, in the years following Bohr's master-
stroke of genius, has given us an insight into the nature of
the atom which could scarcely have been conceived before
1913.

Bohr's work was epoch-making, but no sooner was its
significance realized than the war supervened and put an
almost insuperable barrier in the path of progress. Almost
insuperable, but not quite. As in the field of relativity,
workers in each country went slowly ahead, gathering
what knowledge they could of the work going on in enemy
lands. An important German paper, of which with great

difficulty a copy was brought to England, was photographed by its fortunate recipient and prints were sent round to British physicists. By such means as these was progress made, and it will not be difficult to believe that it was not very rapid. Not until the War was over could scientists return to their work with a single mind and in full communication with one another; and so it happened that the development of the quantum theory, like that of relativity, effectively dates from the establishment of peace.

Now I have spoken of an inner and an outer aspect of scientific history. That is a distinction which we can profitably preserve in discussing the last thirteen years, for the two great developments known as the relativity and quantum theories are associated respectively with these two aspects. Relativity belongs to the outer aspect; that is to say, it is another step in the orderly, progressive discovery of the nature of the world. It is a step taken in accordance with traditional principles and in no way changes either our methods of thought or our notions of the character of science. That may seem strange to those who have been led to think of relativity as a complete revolution of thought, but it is nevertheless the simple fact. The modification which relativity has made in our view of the world is of the nature of the kaleidoscopic changes already referred to, which come about as the direct result of incorporating new phenomena into the company of those already 'explained'. When we examine Nature we find general principles exemplified in particular phenomena, and it is the aim of science to get at those general principles and express them in the simplest way. When that is done we search Nature for verification of their complete generality. So long as we can find such verification the progress of science consists of the absorption of new phenomena into the old category. But one day it may come about that a phenomenon refuses to be absorbed; it does not exemplify but violates the general principle. We have then to realize that the principle was not sufficiently comprehensive, and to displace it by a wider generalization. That is just what is done in the principle of relativity. Newton's laws of motion are found to be only special forms taken by the more general laws under certain restricted conditions, and the more general laws are those of relativity.

There is nothing revolutionary in this; it is the ordinary course of progress. The reason why it is so impressive is that the body of phenomena concerned is so vast. The same kind of thing has occurred on a smaller scale time and again in scientific history, and no suspicion has been aroused that a revolution or even a revolt has been taking place. Relativity is a magnificent achievement, but it is true to type. It changes our view of the world, but it does not change our view-point.

The quantum theory, however, does change our view-point; that is its most significant feature. True, it has an outer aspect of orthodox progress of a highly important kind, but it is in the inner aspect that we see its most vital contribution to the history of science. I have said that the scientist inevitably tends to confuse the ends with the means of his investigation. The quantum theory has shown us that he has been doing that unconsciously for the last hundred years. He has been studying atoms—and, later, electrons and protons—as if they were part of the world of Nature, of the same substance as metals and planets and stars. The quantum theory has shown him that they are instruments of his own invention—elements in terms of which he can make rational statements about the world of sensation and reveal in it a unity which does not exhibit itself on the surface of things, but elements which are essentially beyond observation and even imagination, which do not occupy space or follow the sequence of time, and which fail to conform even to what we have always believed to be necessary laws of thought. In the remainder of this chapter we will try to see how this has happened; the significance of relativity will form one-half of the subject of another chapter.

Now in order to understand the developments of the last thirteen years we must go back almost to the beginning of science. In a Unity History School such a course needs no apology, and I think there will be general agreement with the view that, unless a new discovery can be clearly related to all that has gone before it is either spurious or else imperfectly understood. It is matter for regret that when, as at the present time, startling advances are made, the emphasis in popular presentation is so often laid on the error of the views that have been superseded rather than on the part they have played in making possible the new outlook. The dramatic effect of the unexpected charms away our judgement, and we seek to enhance it by setting the new knowledge in the strongest possible contrast with the old instead of exhibiting it as a natural and inevitable development. We will try not to make that error here, and we will accordingly go back to the time of Newton and see what the great founder of universal physical science conceived to be the scope and purpose of the experimental philosophy.

'All the difficulty of philosophy', he says, 'seems to consist in this, from the phenomena of motions to investigate the forces of Nature, and then from these forces to demonstrate the other phenomena.' Now this is simply Newton's way of describing the process mentioned on a previous page, namely, that of discovering the general principles exemplified in phenomena and then searching Nature for verification of the universality of those principles. It is true that Newton restricts the phenomena to those of motions, and this is important, but we must remember that he is here using the word 'motion' in a wider sense than that usually assigned to it, for elsewhere he includes such phenomena as *fermentations* and *cohesion* among those to be investigated. The main point, however, is that Newton was concerned only with universal principles, which were embodied in phenomena irrespective of the material bodies, the times, and the places concerned in their occurrence. The particular, distinctive features of phenomena did not concern him; they were of the nature of cloaks, hiding the universal from view, and it was the business of philosophy to strip them off. Philosophy had done its work when it had shown that bodies moved in the same way in identical circumstances and exhibited the action of the same forces.

This notion of philosophy, which I have elsewhere called 'abstraction' and which Newton called 'induction from phenomena', seems to us to-day to be unduly restricted. We do not belittle its importance—the theory of relativity is a witness to that—but we do not feel so ready to discard the cloak of particularity when we have removed it from a phenomenon. We want to know more about the detailed, distinctive features of phenomena than the process of induction can tell us, and to obtain such knowledge we find it insufficient to investigate the universal forces of Nature. We cannot proceed without making a *hypothesis*—a supposition of which we have no direct evidence, but which becomes invested with a greater and greater degree of probability as the phenomena which accord with it grow in number and importance. It may happen that one simple hypothesis will suffice to account for a large number of apparently diverse phenomena. In that event, although we may not be able to verify it by direct observation, we do not hesitate to adopt it, because we have added to philosophy, as Newton conceived it, the task of relating together as many as possible of the phenomena of Nature in the simplest way.

Let me repeat the last sentence: we adopt hypotheses 'because we have added to philosophy, as Newton conceived it, the task of relating together as many as possible of the phenomena of Nature in the simplest way'. A few years ago we might have said: 'We adopt hypotheses because we believe them to be true', meaning by 'true' the quality of being a potential phenomenon, not open to direct observation only because of accidental circumstances or the imperfections of our senses. Thus, if we account for the occurrence and propagation of a certain disease by the hypothesis that a particular germ is attacking the body, we often think we imply that the germ is just as real as an elephant, and that we have not seen it only because it is too small or because we have not properly located it or something of that kind. It may be so—in the large majority of cases it probably is—but we must notice that the *actual purpose served* by the hypothesis is simply that of co-ordinating bodily symptoms which we do observe. If we can postulate the *behaviour* of the germ in sufficient detail to account for all its supposed effects, the hypothesis will serve all the purposes of thought and practice that are possible, and the existence or non-existence of the germ becomes a matter of no importance. The *actual* effect of the hypothesis is simply the correlation of observations; its truth is an independent matter, on which we have no right to express an opinion on the basis of its power of correlation alone.

Now Newton was well aware of the possibilities of hypotheses, and he denounced them with all the vehemence of which he was capable. There was reason for his denunciation, for the philosophy of the age immediately preceding that in which he lived had been contaminated by a plethora of hypotheses which encumbered thought without serving any purpose of correlation. Each observed fact was attributed to a specific cause, so that the world of phenomena became virtually doubled; to each manifest phenomenon was added an occult generating principle which did nothing but account for that particular phenomenon. Against this practice Newton set up his philosophy of induction from phenomena.

'These Principles' [gravity, cohesion, &c.], he writes, 'I consider, not as occult Qualities, supposed to result from the specifick Forms of Things, but as general Laws of Nature, by which the Things themselves are form'd; their Truth appearing to us by Phænomena, though their Causes be not yet discover'd. For these are manifest Qualities, and their Causes only are occult. And the *Aristotelians* gave the Name of occult Qualities, not to manifest Qualities, but to such Qualities only as they supposed to lie hid in Bodies, and to be the unknown Causes of manifest Effects: Such as would be the Causes of Gravity, and of magnetick and electrick Attractions, and of Fermentations, if we should suppose that these Forces or Actions arose from Qualities unknown to us, and uncapable of being discovered and made manifest. Such occult Qualities put a stop to the Improvement of natural Philosophy, and therefore of late Years have been rejected. To tell us that every Species of Things is endow'd with an occult specifick Quality by which it acts and produces manifest Effects, is to tell us nothing: But to derive two or three general Principles of Motion from Phænomena, and afterwards to tell us how the Properties and Actions of all corporeal Things follow from those manifest Principles, would be a very great step in Philosophy, though the Causes of those Principles were not yet discover'd.'

'I frame no hypotheses.'; he says again, 'For whatever is not deduc'd from the phænomena, is to be called an hypothesis; and hypotheses, whether metaphysical or physical, whether of occult qualities or mechanical, have no place in experimental philosophy.'

Now if we examine these words of Newton's in order to determine precisely what he objected to in the formulation of hypotheses, we shall find that it was simply the confusion of things which were *observed* to exist with things which were *imagined* to exist. He did not object to imagination: he himself invented force and gravitation, and there is a sense in which they might be called hypotheses. But he never supposed that force and gravitation had a physical reality of the same kind as that of a piece of matter. They were conceptions in terms of which he could frame principles which were incarnated in all the phenomena of motion. The physical reality corresponding to gravitation he called the *cause* of gravitation, and admitted that he knew nothing about it. He therefore left it outside his philosophy altogether. He included that quality of a hypothesis which enabled it to correlate phenomena, but excluded that quality which we may call 'actuality' or 'reality' or 'truth'.

We see, therefore, that Newton realized quite clearly what we spoke of just now as a revelation of the last few years. He saw that it was perfectly legitimate for philosophers to invent notions for the purpose of correlating phenomena, but that it was not legitimate for them to endow those notions with the actuality of phenomena, or indeed to suppose anything at all about them beyond what was specifically required by the facts of observation. It is easy to become enslaved to words, and by speaking generally of 'hypotheses' we are apt to overlook this distinction. The consequence is that Newton's attitude to hypotheses has been hotly debated between those who point to his words on one hand and those who point to his practice on the other. There is no inconsistency when we distinguish between the pragmatic and the hypostatic aspects of hypotheses, but it is only lately that scientists generally have realized what Newton saw 250 years ago.

The fault, however, is not entirely ours. We are the heirs of generations in which hypotheses have successfully dominated scientific activity; Newton followed an age of which they had been the bane. The failure to heed the warning of Newton must be attributed to the physicists of 100 years ago who returned to the medieval practice of inventing occult qualities. They did so, it is true, for the purpose of correlating phenomena, and thus they simplified Nature instead of complicating it in the manner of the Aristotelians, but they signally failed to realize what Newton had emphasized by word and deed, that a hypothetical quality was of a different nature from a phenomenon and was not to be supposed actual or to possess any of the attributes of actuality until it was observed.

The time of which we are speaking was the time when atoms first entered seriously into physics. Certain facts of observation which appeared superficially to be quite independent of one another could be brought into simple relation if it was supposed that all bodies were ultimately made up of very minute discrete particles. These particles could not be observed, and there was no direct fact of observation which suggested their existence. The reason for thinking of them was that if they existed they would account rationally for, and connect logically together, a large variety of phenomena. Scientists accordingly made the hypothesis that each chemically elementary body was composed of a multitude of precisely similar 'atoms'—indivisible particles far too small for observation, but otherwise of the same character as observed bodies and possessing all the qualities—such as mass, extension, gravitation, and what not—which had been found to be universally characteristic of ordinary sensible matter.

Now from what has just been said we can see that in so doing they went definitely beyond what Newton considered permissible. The fault was not in supposing the existence of atoms; it was in supposing that these atoms, although unobservable, must inevitably possess the same properties as phenomena. It is very fortunate for our understanding of this point that Newton himself held an atomic theory, and we can directly compare it with the hypothesis we are now discussing. Newton pointed out that since, when bodies were cut up into smaller and smaller parts, the limit was set, not by a change in the properties of the bodies but by the grossness of the instruments of division, it was reasonable to suppose that still further division was inherently possible, and that since the particles so obtained would be parts of observed bodies it was reasonable to suppose that they also would have the qualities of observed bodies. They would not be hypothetical existences such as the Aristotelian occult qualities or the cause of his own gravitation; they would be potential phenomena which an advance in instrument-making might make actual. But the atoms of the early nineteenth century were not so arrived at step by step from phenomena; they were *a priori* postulates and, so far from being directly 'deduced from the phenomena', they were given one characteristic which was not that of phenomena at all, namely indivisibility. On this point the comparison with Newton is very instructive, for he draws the clearest possible distinction between what we imagine and what we observe. He says:

'That the divided but contiguous particles of bodies may be separated from one another is matter of observation; and, in the particles that remain undivided, our *minds*[1] are able to distinguish yet lesser parts, as is mathematically demonstrated. But whether the parts so distinguished, and not yet divided, may, by the powers of Nature, be *actually*[1] divided and separated from one another, we cannot certainly determine. Yet, had we the proof of but one experiment that any undivided particle, in breaking a hard and solid body, suffered a division, we might . . . conclude that the undivided as well as the divided particles may be divided and actually separated to infinity.'

It is clear, therefore, that the 'atoms' of Newton were simply small particles of ordinary bodies whose existence was deduced from the fact that we can cut bodies into parts down to the limits set by our means of division. The atoms of the modern atomic theory, on the other hand, were imaginary entities, conceived *a priori* for the purpose of explaining or correlating phenomena which had

[1] The italics are mine.

nothing to do with the process of cutting. Newton's atoms
had the characteristics of phenomena because they were
phenomena in everything but being separate from one
another. The modern atoms were given the characteristics of phenomena because it was not realized that they
were inventions.

The effect of giving these hypothetical atoms the characteristics of phenomena was, naturally, to lead to the
belief that they *were* potential phenomena. It was thought
that if you could only magnify matter sufficiently you
would see them, although, of course, no one would venture
to dogmatize about what they would look like. Later,
when some idea of their size was obtained, it was realized
that they could not be seen by a microscope whatever its
magnifying power might be, because they were so much
smaller than a wave of light that visibility had to be denied
them. But that raised no doubts about their essential
reality. By that time scientists had got beyond testing
actuality by observability, and had made of it a metaphysical notion, so that the attribute of being real was an
ultimate one of which no definition in physical terms could
be given. Although they could not be observed, atoms
were still 'real', and there was no more to be said about
the matter.

I have spoken of the 'size' of atoms: how could this
be found when the atoms could not be observed? The
answer illustrates very forcibly what the nature of these
atoms was. The size was found not by any kind of measurement of length, but from experiments on the conduction
of heat among other things. In order that the observed
rate of conduction of heat along bodies should be expres-
sible in terms of the motions of the atoms it was necessary
that the influence of an atom should extend over a certain
range, and that range was expressed as the 'size' of the
atom. Nothing could illustrate more clearly the facts, first,
that the atoms were inventions for the purpose of inter-

preting phenomena, and secondly, that they were given the attribute of extension in space not because they necessarily possessed it, but because they were instinctively looked upon as of the nature of phenomena. 'That all bodies are impenetrable,' wrote Newton, 'we gather not from reason, but from sensation.' That the nineteenth-century atoms were extensive, however, was gathered not from sensation or from reason, but from an intuition which we now know to be false. It is true that the experiments on the conduction of heat were not the only ones which gave a sphere of influence to the atom which was interpreted as its 'size'; experiments of quite different character gave the same 'size'. But that in no way justified the ascription of extension to the atom; it simply meant that the atomic theory, as a conception, was capable consistently of correlating widely different phenomena. If different phenomena had given contradictory results the theory would have been discredited; the fact that they gave concordant results established its usefulness, but it did not justify its misinterpretation.

In time, as we all know, the 'indivisibility' of the atom had to be abandoned, but that was merely a literal modification of the theory. An atom could be broken into parts, which were called *protons* and *electrons*, but it then ceased to be an atom of its own particular element. An atom of iron still remained the ultimate particle of iron. From the point of view of the *effectiveness* of the theory the disintegration of the atom was an advance of the first importance, but from the point of view of *interpretation* it was negligible. Physicists continued to look on an atom as a potential phenomenon, and concentrated their attention on determining its structure out of the elementary constituents. Not until about twenty years ago did they obtain even a temporarily satisfactory solution of this problem. At that time Rutherford put, forward the now famous 'solar-system' model, according to which the atom

consisted of a number of electrons, or units of negative
electricity, circulating round a central condensed nucleus
of mixed protons and electrons, with the former—the
units of positive electricity—predominating. It was with
this model that it first became possible to interpret the
phenomena of emission and absorption of radiation, and
the progress of the attempt to do so, as has already been
said, is the characteristic feature of the post-war period.

We have almost reached the end of our allotted space,
and have only just begun to touch the years with which
we are concerned. Very bad management it appears, but
in truth it is so in appearance only. The spirit of the years
of peace has permeated everything here written, for the
soul of the recent progress—the inner aspect, as I have
called it—is the new vision it has given us of the course of
scientific history. We thought the atom was a part of the
world to be examined; we find now that it is an instrument
for examining the world of phenomena. We have consequently to reinterpret the history of physics in the new
light, and this brief account is such a reinterpretation. It
could not have been written before 1913. Although nothing
has been said of the details of what has happened since, the
omission is not an evasion of our main task. In the little
space that remains we will try to see in outline how it has
been brought home to us that the atom is a creature of the
world of thought and not of the world of sense. It will not
matter that the description is condensed into a few short
sentences.

The solar-system model of the atom was a triumph of
experimental and imaginative skill, but it had one fatal
defect. The laws of electro-magnetism showed that it was
inherently unstable and in a small fraction of a second
would destroy itself. There was no escape from this difficulty except by recognizing that the atom was not subject
to the laws of electro-magnetism, and this is what Bohr
had the genius and the courage to perceive. It may seem

a slight thing, but to physicists who had been born and bred in the belief that atoms were real, potential phenomena, and to whom obedience to the laws of electromagnetism was as inevitable as gravitation towards the earth or extension in space seems to ordinary people, the idea was almost unthinkable, a flagrant denial of common sense. Nevertheless, only by such a supposition could the atom, and therefore the whole material world, be saved from instantaneous annihilation. That was the first indication that atoms were of a different nature from observed bodies.

For a time this one denial of common sense was sufficient. The work of correlation went merrily on, but soon new difficulties began to accumulate. These were found to be insuperable without a further break with common sense. The electrons of which atoms were composed had to be regarded for some purposes as particles and for others as waves, and no reconciliation between these opposing views was found to be possible. Some phenomena inevitably required that the electron was a wave spreading out into space; other phenomena equally inevitably required that it was concentrated into a tiny particle. The necessary conclusion is that the electron is not something which can properly be said to have extension in space.

Shortly after this another discovery was made: not only was the electron non-spatial; it was non-temporal also. Its behaviour could not be predicted: it could be rationalized after it had taken place, but not before. In other words, the electron or atom seemed to be able to foresee events which we could not foresee and to act accordingly, so that to us in our ignorance it seemed to be undetermined. All these abnormal qualities are now generally admitted to be characteristic of the particles of which atoms are composed.

It appears very fantastic, all this, but what is the natural meaning? Simply that atoms are pure conceptions, of a different nature from phenomena. They are the mental units out of which we build up rationally a description of the world which agrees with observation, but they themselves are neither actually nor potentially a part of the world of observation. When this is realized—and it is not, I think, difficult to realize—all the apparent unintelligibility of modern atomic physics vanishes. We have difficulty in picturing an atom with such extraordinary qualities, but that is simply because we try to picture it as a piece of matter. We do not find the conception of virtue difficult because it does not occupy space, or the conception of courage incomprehensible because it is unaffected by an electro-magnetic field. Let us once grasp the idea that atoms are simply mental concepts, and we shall not expect them to conform to our notions of space and time. The things which are seen are temporal, but the things which are not seen are eternal—that is to say, not indefinitely persistent in time but removed outside it altogether.

One final word of warning. It has taken us 100 years to liberate atoms from the characteristics of phenomena. Unless we are very careful, it will take us not 100 minutes to enslave phenomena to the newly-discovered characteristics of atoms. The fact that atoms, if they are to continue to be of use in correlating phenomena, must be held to be undetermined, in no way requires that the world of experience is undetermined. We sometimes hear that according to the new physics Nature is capricious and knows nothing of regularity or order. The whole of experience stands in direct contradiction to this, and we must never forget that all we know and can ever know about atoms is derived ultimately from experience. Nothing which experience teaches us indirectly can violate her direct utterance. Nature is one thing, and the conceptions which we employ to rationalize it are another. We have erred in the past by imposing the characteristics of the one on the other; let us not, on learning our mistake, err again in the opposite way.

BOOKS FOR REFERENCE

G. P. Thomson. *The Atom.* Thornton Butterworth.

C. G. Darwin. *The New Conceptions of Matter.* Bell.

M. Planck. *The Universe in the Light of Modern Physics.* Allen & Unwin.

A. S. Eddington. *The Nature of the Physical World.* Cambridge University Press.

J. H. Jeans. *The Mysterious Universe.* Cambridge University Press.

H. Dingle. *Science and Human Experience.* Williams & Norgate.

III

THE UNIVERSE

By HERBERT DINGLE

IT may seem superfluous to begin an account of the universe by saying that the subject is a very big one, but actually the significance of such a remark would lie not in its obviousness but in the question of its truth. 'Big' is a relative term, and from our point of view the standard of comparison is the idea we held in November 1918. Now when we ask whether, judged by that standard, the universe according to our present ideas is great or small, we may answer with equal truth, 'It is very great'; or, 'It is infinitely small'. In saying this we are not propounding a metaphysical paradox or indulging in one of those relativistic extravagances which the general public has resigned itself to regarding as profound because it cannot understand them. The remark springs from neither of these things, but simply indicates the fact that the word 'universe', even in astronomy, is used in at least two quite different senses.

This ambiguity is very unfortunate, and so far as this chapter is concerned we will remove it by speaking of the universe only as the equivalent of the whole of space and its physical contents. That is a permissible and common use of the term, but there is also another common use which is perhaps not so clearly permissible. We have known, for some time that the system of stars in which we are situated is a more or less isolated unit in space, and we believe now that in other parts of space there are somewhat similar isolated systems. It is common to speak of these systems, including our own, as 'island universes', and when we are discussing our own system we frequently refer to it as 'the universe'. That is a liberty of which, for present purposes, we shall not avail ourselves;

we will speak of the local congregation of stars as our
'stellar system'.

The remark, then, that the universe as we now conceive
it is much larger and infinitely smaller than the universe
we visualized in 1918, becomes translated into this: the
universe is infinitely smaller but our stellar system is very
much larger. The phrase 'infinitely smaller' may seem a
mere colloquial exaggeration. It is not, however; it is the
literal truth. We thought formerly that space was infinite
in extent; we believe now that it is finite, and, whatever
dimensions we may assign to it, a finite space is infinitely
smaller than infinite space because it would take an
infinite number of finite spaces to occupy infinity.

The idea of a finite space seems impossible to hold. It is
notoriously difficult to conceive how space can possibly do
other than extend to infinity, and the objector in self-
defence feels inclined to retort: How can you possibly
know that space is finite when your telescopes can pierce
at most to only a very small fraction of its extent? The
answer raises an important point. When, in a former
chapter, we were considering the atom we were almost
entirely in a world of ideas. Physics accumulated its basic
phenomena long ago, and its main task now is to make
order out of them. Apples were observed to fall long before
Newton's day, and the wanderings of the Moon are ancient
history. What Newton did was not to discover these
things but to correlate them by finding out the general law
which they both expressed, and physicists since his day
have been engaged in similar tasks. Of course, discoveries
in physics have been made and continue to be made, and
it is impossible to exaggerate their importance, but they
are highly recondite. They are found from experiments
made with refined apparatus under very special conditions
—conditions which would never occur in Nature if man
were not there to order things to his will. Furthermore,
these experiments are always conducted at the instigation

of some previously-formed general idea arising from the consideration of the more obvious phenomena. Physics, we may say in broad terms, has its fundamental facts complete; its work consists in finding how they can be rationally related with one another.

But astronomy is in a totally different position. The facts it has are probably very few compared with those yet to be discovered, not by abstruse experiment but by simple observation. The construction of a larger telescope might multiply our knowledge of the universe a hundred-fold merely by its direct revelations. The astronomer therefore has a dual task; he has to go on increasing his knowledge of the facts of the universe and, at the same time, deduce from the facts which he has already learnt the general principles which underlie them and which will automatically be embodied in whatever he may in future discover.

An analogy will, perhaps, help to make the situation clear, although, like all analogies, it must be applied with considerable caution. We may liken the astronomer to the spectator of a game, who is interested in the course of the play and also anxious to learn the rules of the game of which he is ignorant. The rules are universal principles, expressed in every incident that occurs, and the spectator will not necessarily require to see the whole of the game in order to arrive at them. Some may be easy of detection, and having formed a notion of them from the early events, he will look to see them obeyed in all that follows. In this way he will check the accuracy of his generalization. When he is acting in this respect he is like the physicist or the theoretical astronomer. But whatever the rules are, they do not determine the course of the game; there are infinite possibilities, all of them consistent with the rules, but none of them identical with another. To describe the game fully he has to watch as well as think. When he is acting in this respect he is like the practical astronomer. And so it is that while the spectator may be in total ignorance of what course the game will take in its ultimate stages, he may say with confidence that it will necessarily be subject to certain restrictions which his knowledge of some of the rules prescribes. Similarly, the astronomer may not have pierced to the uttermost recesses of space, but he concludes nevertheless that space has the character of finitude.

In the last thirteen years remarkable progress has been made both in mapping out the structure of the universe by observation and in deducing from our little knowledge the general characteristics which the universe must possess. We will divide our pages as fairly as possible between the two kinds of research, but there is one general remark which must be made at once. Limits of space absolutely prohibit any attempt at *explanation* of the progress; we can only *describe* it, and the description must be of the barest possible kind.

The general laws which the universe, whatever it is like, must exhibit are embodied in the principle of relativity and its later developments. Much of the evidence for this comes from physics, where the minuteness of the range of observation compared with that of astronomy is more than compensated for by the exactness of measurement which is possible. We will not venture on the physical aspects of the theory, however, but only on its astronomical, or rather its cosmogonical, aspects. In the early days it was realized that the new views which the theory involved would probably require that space returned on itself, so to speak, like the surface of a ball. If we imagine a two-dimensional creature walking continuously in the same direction over the surface of a sphere, we can see that he will ultimately return to his starting-point. Having no idea of what we, with a knowledge of a third dimension, call the *curvature* of the sphere, he thinks he is travelling in a straight line, and if he is sufficiently clear-headed he will realize that the surface of the sphere is not an infinite plane, as he might have thought from observation of a small region, but is a finite area, although it has no sharp boundary over which he might conceive himself to step. According to the theory of relativity our familiar three-dimensional space is to us like the surface of the sphere is to such a creature: it is curved in a dimension of which we have no cognizance, and if we could continue travelling in the same direction for an indefinite time we should at last return to our starting-point. We cannot perhaps imagine this, but that does not matter very much. We can at least see that the apparent obviousness of the contrary is an illusion. If we take flight upwards from the Earth with some infallible compass to guide us in a straight line, a time will come when we shall have lost sight of everything familiar. We shall be travelling on in totally new regions, unable to imagine what we shall encounter next. It is not inconceivable that after a time we shall find ourselves near the Earth again. Our first thought will be that our compass is wrong, but unquestionable tests may deny us that escape from the fact. It is perfectly conceivable, therefore, that the seemingly incredible may happen, and what is conceivable is not obviously impossible.

But, after all, the ability to imagine the state of affairs is not of the first importance. Thought is a safer investigator of Nature than imagination, and the character which thought requires space to have in order to harmonize the facts which we know demands that the extent of space is not infinite. This is the first cosmogonical implication of relativity.

We have likened space to the surface of a sphere, but the analogy must not be taken too literally. We might have used the surface of an egg, or even of a pear, and still have retained all the characteristics of the surface which are required for the analogy. The fact that space is re-entrant on itself leaves open the question whether its curvature is

uniform everywhere or not, and if not, how it varies as we
travel outwards. It also says nothing about the size of
the universe or of what goes on in it. Many possible
answers may be given to these questions, and before the
end of the war two plausible attempts were made to
introduce a little more detail into the general view of the
universe than was contained in the mere assertion of its
finitude. These attempts were made by Einstein and de
Sitter respectively. I will not attempt to describe in
relativistic language what their conceptions involved, but,
following Eddington, I will translate it back into familiar
Newtonian language. That will not only have the advantage of being intelligible but it will also serve to show
that the relativistic way of looking at things is not a metaphysical speculation in contrast to the Newtonian examination of facts, but is essentially another (and, as physicists
recognize, a better) interpretation of facts which are just
as concrete as those considered by Newton.

According to Newton's law of gravitation, every piece of
matter in the universe attracts every other piece of matter
with a force which varies inversely as the square of the
distance between them. Relativity describes the same
phenomenon, not in terms of force at all, but in terms of
the characteristics of a medium called 'space-time'. We
will, as I have said, speak of forces. Now it turns out that
the additional requirement of relativity—that the universe
is finite—implies the existence of another force, of repulsion this time, which varies *directly* as the distance
between bodies; that is to say, the farther apart bodies are,
the greater is this repulsive force between them. For
bodies separated by distances such as those to which we
have been accustomed in physics and astronomy, gravitation is so much the more powerful influence that the other
force has not even been suspected, on observational
grounds, of existing, but it is clear from the nature of the
forces that as we recede from a body its ordinary New-

tonian force of attraction diminishes while its new force of repulsion increases. The question therefore arises: Are the size of the universe and the relative magnitudes of these two factors such that the repulsive force will overcome gravitation at great distances or not? Now this is a question which could be answered by observation if our instruments were powerful enough, but at the time of which we are thinking, at least, the necessary observations were not available. Einstein and de Sitter accordingly put forward two possibilities which the equations of relativity suggested.

Einstein assumed that, taking the universe as a whole, matter was more or less evenly distributed in such a way that gravitation and the repulsive force just balanced one another everywhere. Now this seems absurd for, as we have just seen, throughout the part of the universe which we have been accustomed to study, gravitation is supreme, and there is no evidence at all of a repulsive force. But we must remember that, on the scale of the universe, a region like that of the solar system, or even our stellar system, is negligible; it becomes a mere point. The predominance of gravitation there is a mere local turbulence, no more indicative of the general character of the universe than the Alps are of the surface of the Earth. Leaving that local phenomenon out of account and considering the full extent of space, the Einstein world is such that matter is evenly distributed throughout it with just the right density to keep it static, its parts neither attracting nor repelling one another.

This, of course, would be a very special sort of condition, and it was suggested only as a possible approximation to the truth. De Sitter's universe also was a kind of extreme possibility, and again was suggested only as an approximation. De Sitter conceived a universe in which matter was so thinly distributed that it could be neglected. In that case gravitation effectively vanished and only the repulsive force was left. De Sitter's world was therefore being dissipated rapidly in all directions, only there was so little of it that it was not worth considering.

We will deal later with more recently acquired observational evidence on the matter. At present we are confining ourselves to 'what we have called the general rules of the game, and at the stage of which we are speaking the spectator is in doubt about certain important rules; the Einstein and de Sitter universes are two alternative guesses, inspired by the part of the game which he has witnessed. Now in the last two or three years, apart altogether from observation, he has realized that the Einstein universe cannot possibly be a permanent representation of actuality because it is essentially unstable. Even if the universe began in such a way, the slightest disturbance would upset the balance which could never be recovered: the universe would inevitably tend towards the de Sitter condition.

The universe we at present conceive is therefore between the Einstein and de Sitter approximations. Supposing it started as an Einstein world—which seems more likely than anything else—we must then imagine that some trifle, we know not what as yet, destroyed the equilibrium and that it started to expand. It is expanding now, at an increasingly rapid rate. In terms of Newtonian conceptions the repulsive force overcomes gravitation at great distances. According to the relativistic view, the sphere to the surface of which we likened space is a balloon which is being inflated: the distances between marks on the surface, which we may take to represent pieces of matter, get greater as the inflation proceeds. It must be understood that this means that *space* is expanding, not merely that material objects are getting farther apart in a constant space. The balloon itself is being blown up, and just as it takes a fly longer to crawl round it as it gets larger, so it would take a traveller, moving at a given speed, longer to girdle space the later he makes the journey. Indeed, unless his speed exceeds a certain value he will never complete the circuit, for space will be expanding faster than he is moving through it. The indications at present are that even the speed of light—the greatest speed possible for a material body—would be insufficient to permit the complete circuit of space now, although it would have allowed the journey in past ages, and it must be remembered that the rate of expansion is still getting greater as time goes on.

It is important to realize that the expansion of space is not a metaphysical notion, as might at first be imagined: it simply expresses facts of observation of precisely the same kind as the facts familiar to us in everyday life. Difficulty is sometimes experienced in realizing this because we cannot imagine anything for space to expand into. We must remember, however, that facts capable of experimental verification are not necessarily imaginable. The expansion of space is simply a way of expressing the following facts. If we set out a straight line into space and continue it until it returns into itself, and then measure the total length of this line, we shall get a certain result. This is a process which can be conducted in a manner essentially similar to that employed in measuring the length of a cricket pitch or the distance of a star—though the details of the method used may not be identical. If, now, we repeat the operation at a later time we shall get a larger result, and if we repeat it again at a still later time we shall get a still larger result. We can express these facts by saying that the universe is expanding, because the length of our re-entrant line is the length of the 'circumference' of space. The experiment has not been made in this way, but that is simply because of practical difficulties—not at all because the process is in any way occult. If, instead of trying to imagine the process of expansion, we simply think of this familiar kind of operation, we shall realize that the conception is no more metaphysical than the ordinary conceptions of terrestrial surveying. If the reader insists on picturing the process as a whole in his mind, he may express the same facts, as Eddington has well pointed out, by regarding the universe as fixed in size, and his measuring rods as continuously contracting. This would account legitimately, and in an equivalent way, for the experimental results, and would perhaps be more intelligible to the ordinary mind, though a philosopher might find it as difficult to conceive of bodies collapsing inwards as of space expanding outwards. The main point, however, is that the idea of an expanding space merely expresses actual or potential facts of experiment, and it is not necessary for scientific purposes to clothe it with picturesque images, although the words employed to describe it of necessity suggest such images.

This notion of the expanding universe is one of the two great contributions of recent years to our knowledge of the rules of the game. It is derived not from *direct* observational evidence—although, as we shall see, there is now such evidence of its validity, which enables us to make tentative estimates of the size, age, and rate of expansion of the universe—but from generalization of facts gathered mainly from our solar system. There is infinite variety possible for the structure of the universe, and which structure is actual can be determined only by observation, but whatever it may be it must conform to the general rule of a finite expanding space. We must again emphasize the fact that this rule is not something particular about the universe as it happens to be, but is a general characteristic of all possible universes. It does not follow that it is established beyond possibility of error. It is quite possible that some mistake has been made, just as a spectator of a football match who could observe only the region round the goalkeeper might form erroneous ideas of the general rules. But the point is that it does not depend on the particular plan on which our universe has been constructed. The law of gravitation is true or untrue independently of how many double stars there are which exhibit its operation or of where those stars happen to be. In the same way, the expanding universe is independent of all such structural considerations.

I have called the idea of the expanding universe one of the two great cosmogonical advances of recent years. We can afford only the briefest mention of the second, because we must hasten on to the description of the universe itself. The principle of relativity has given us a new view of matter, according to which matter and radiation are forms of the same thing. This could not have been found out directly from observation because we have never observed any transformation of one of these entities into the other. We have therefore, as it were, deduced a rule of the game which the players have so far had no occasion to employ before us. But it may be that in another part of the field this rule plays a crucial part in directing the course of the game; or, in other words, that somewhere in the universe matter may be changing into radiation or radiation into matter. Now that we know that such an event is permissible we are in a more advantageous position than before for dealing with phenomena which are superficially very mysterious, only we must be on our guard against allowing the mere possibility of the process to predispose us too strongly to assume its actuality. Operations may be permitted which the players are not skilful enough to perform. And here I must leave the general rules and proceed to an account of the particular universe which we inhabit.

In 1918 the great 100-inch telescope was erected at Mount Wilson Observatory, California, and in the same year the 73-inch telescope of the Dominion Observatory, Victoria, British Columbia, began its exploration of the heavens. Most of the advances now to be described are the direct result of the work of these magnificent instruments, and how important is the fact of world peace is strikingly exhibited by the fact that it is only by the greatest good fortune that they have been available for investigation. The discs of which their mirrors are made, which took several years to prepare, were cast at the St. Gobain works in France—the disc for the Canadian telescope, in fact, was despatched a bare week before the outbreak of war. In the calamity which followed, the works of the St. Gobain Co. were completely destroyed.

At the end of the War our ideas of the stellar system were on the eve of a great change. Here is a diagrammatic summary of what might be considered the orthodox view of that time. It is taken from a lecture by Professor H. D. Curtis, then of the Lick Observatory, which was delivered in 1917 and published in 1919, so that it is fairly representative of the beginning of the years of peace.

100,000 ± Spiral Nebulae
Distance unknown
.

.

.

The Milky Way and stellar universe
is believed to be roughly lens-shaped and about
3,000 by 30,000 or more light-years in extent. In this space
occur nearly all the stars, nearly all the diffuse nebulosities, nearly all
the planetary nebulae, nearly all new stars, nearly all
clusters, nearly all the variable stars, etc., but
NO SPIRAL NEBULAE.

.

.

.

100,000 ± Spiral Nebulae
Distance unknown

Not merely the matter but also the form of this summary is significant. The central portion is intended to represent a section of our stellar system, which was then and is now

believed to be a flat disc-shaped structure. This idea
dates from the time of Sir William Herschel, whose drawing of the stellar system is shown below.

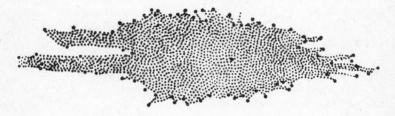

In 1918, then, we thought of our system as isolated in
space, containing everything but the spiral nebulae, and
having a diameter of about 30,000 light-years. (A light-
year is the distance light travels in a year—about six
million million miles.) It will be noticed that Professor
Curtis puts against the spiral nebulae, 'distance unknown',
and we must add that because of this fact he was by no
means expressing the general opinion in putting even
these objects outside the stellar system. There were
widely differing views of their character and distances, and
there was evidence of considerable weight for the idea that
they also formed part of our system and were, in fact, the
original material out of which stars were made.

But about this time Professor Shapley, then at Mount
Wilson Observatory, was carrying on some remarkable
researches on the globular clusters and other objects on the
confines of the system, and was forming estimates of their
distances on somewhat bold principles which have since
been accorded much more general approval than they could
claim at first. As a result of his work, Professor Shapley
came to the conclusion that the stellar system was far
larger than had previously been supposed—at least ten
times as extensive, in fact, as it is represented in the
diagram of Professor Curtis. For some time the question

was keenly debated, but although the matter is not yet beyond doubt, the balance of opinion is, I think, strongly in favour of the larger dimensions. While we cannot give any precise figure for the diameter of our system we can at least say that it must be measured in hundreds of thousands of light-years. That is what I had in mind when I opened this chapter by saying that our stellar system is very large compared with what was believed thirteen years ago.

So much for its dimensions; what of its form? That is still very largely in doubt, but one thing is certain—the various objects in it are distributed with a very high degree of irregularity. It is a conglomeration of clusters and groups of stars of various sizes and complexity, interspersed with a large amount of nebulous matter. If we were to take a journey from the solar system through the Milky Way we should find that for some distance the stars would be thinning out until we might come to a comparatively empty space and then farther on enter another cloud of stars. The reason for this is that the Sun is in the midst of what we call 'the local cluster'. In the early days of these investigations this local cluster deceived us into thinking it was the whole stellar system, but, thanks to a line of research begun by Professor Charlier of Lund, we do not make that mistake now. If we could withdraw from the stellar system altogether and look back on it, we should see it as an agglomeration of clouds and clusters of stars, possibly having a regularity towards which at this stage of our investigation we are only dimly feeling our way. The stellar system at present appears as a more or less haphazard grouping, but there are hints of orderly arrangement which the future will doubtless make more definite.

In the catalogue of contents of our system which Professor Curtis drew up there are, as we now know, two omissions. There are doubtless more, but of these two we have become aware during the years with which we are concerned. One is an extensive, tenuous distribution of gaseous matter which, so far as we can tell, permeates the whole system. It can be observed only by examining the distant stars. Their light comes to us through thousands of light-years of space, and in the journey it traverses just enough of this unimaginably rarefied material to suffer a slight absorption of certain constituents which we recognize as characteristic of the element calcium. The intervening material is not necessarily calcium alone, for there are reasons why calcium would probably reveal itself more readily than other substances, so that we have to recognize that interstellar space is not quite empty but is more or less uniformly filled with this cloudy material. According to one view, the diffuse nebulae are merely local condensations of this substance, visible only on account of their relatively great density. How tenuous the cosmical cloud is might be gathered from the following remark by Sir Arthur Eddington, who first interpreted the evidence for its existence: 'The cosmic matter in a volume as large as the earth could be packed in a suitcase and easily carried with one hand.'

The other constituent of the stellar system is not matter but radiation. Before the War there was some evidence of an extremely penetrating radiation in our atmosphere, very small in amount but capable of penetrating greater thickness of material than even the hardest of our X-rays. The last thirteen years have shown that this radiation is not generated on the Earth or even in the solar system, but belongs to the stellar system and perhaps the whole universe. We are still very much in the dark about its origin and nature, but we are forced to recognize that it is probably an extremely important factor of the stellar system. Some regard it as evidence that the conversion of matter into radiation is an accomplished fact and that it is itself the product of the process. Others again look upon it as evidence of the building up of heavier elements from lighter. At present we cannot say with confidence what it means—more facts of observation are required—but we have no longer any doubt of its existence and importance.

Another great discovery of the last few years is that this whole stellar system, with its stars, nebulae, and permeating cloud, is rotating about its centre. This conclusion, arrived at by the same method as that which has lately inspired general conviction of the rotation, was reached as long ago as 1871 by Gyldén, a Swede. His work, however, was in advance of its time and met with no response from other astronomers. It is only quite lately that the rotation of the stellar system has been given general consideration, and that mainly through the pioneer work of Professor Lindblad of Stockholm and Dr. Oort of Leiden, and the observations of Dr. Plaskett of Victoria, B.C. The results can best be described by giving a general account of the stellar system as we now conceive it. It will be understood, of course, that the figures are exceedingly rough, but they are probably of the right order of magnitude, for independent methods of arriving at them give fairly accordant results.

The stellar system is a flat, apparently irregularly distributed company of stars and nebulae with a diameter of a few hundred thousand light-years. It contains something like 100,000 million stars, more or less similar to the Sun, and is spinning about its centre, not like a rigid body in which all parts complete a revolution in the same time, but in such a way that the nearer a star is to the centre the faster does it move. Our solar system is far from the centre, but the distance is very uncertain, the estimates ranging from 30,000 to 80,000 light-years. We take about 250 million years to perform a complete revolution; the stars nearer to the centre take, as has already been said, a shorter, and those more distant a longer, time. Since the

Earth became a solid body it has travelled five or six times round the system. The centre itself is in the direction of the constellation Sagittarius—a region which is near the most densely crowded portion of the Milky Way and which would be still brighter were it not for dark obscuring matter hiding the more distant parts from our view. The system thus contemplated exceeds in grandeur all previous conceptions. We have made the universe finite, but a finitude containing such systems as this is almost more impressive than infinity.

Mention was made just now of new methods by which Shapley had measured the dimensions of the stellar system. Those methods are capable of an even wider application, and they have been directed to the problem of measuring the distances of the spiral nebulae. Only a few of the nearer of these nebulae are at present within reach of the methods—in fact, it is only the nearer ones that are within reach of our telescopes at all—but the results are sufficient to settle once for all the question whether the nebulae are within the confines of our stellar system or not. The answer is definitely that they are not; the nearest of them is nearly a million light-years away. The light by which we see it started on its journey nearly a million years ago.

This figure shows at once that the nebula is outside our system, but it tells us something more; it tells us the dimensions of the nebula, for by observing how large the object appears we can calculate from the distance how large it actually is. We find as a result that the nebula is smaller indeed than our stellar system, but not incomparably so. The few nearest of the nebulae whose distances we can measure by individual methods are of the order of a quarter or thereabouts of the diameter of our stellar system—veritable stellar systems themselves so far as their size goes. But before we can conclude that they are stellar systems we must know of what they are composed. In the early days of the post-war period they might

THE NEAREST SPIRAL NEBULA
(M 33 in Triangulum)

have been gas or nebulous material or congregations of stars too far away for their individual constituents to be recognized—the evidence was insufficient to arouse general agreement on even their most probable composition. We are in a different position now. The outlying portions of the few nearest of them have been definitely resolved into stars by the 100-inch telescope, so that we may look upon them with confidence as 'island universes', to use the familiar phrase—systems of stars, if not precisely similar to, yet strongly resembling our stellar system.

This discovery clearly opens up a whole new field of inquiry. We have now to determine not only the organization of stars within the stellar system, but also the organization of stellar systems within the universe. If the spiral nebulae are actually of the same character as our stellar system it follows that we are in a spiral nebula, and the apparent irregularity of distribution of our stars is simply due to the fact that, being situated inside the system—possibly in one of the spiral arms (see illustration), since our position is so eccentric—we cannot detect its true form without long and detailed observation and analysis. The conclusion is tempting, but it is not to be accepted hastily. In some parts of space we find what appear to be organizations of spiral nebulae—groups of, say, four or five, more or less intimately related to one another. The large dimensions of our system compared with those of the spirals nearest to us suggest that perhaps our apparently irregular system is another such group. Professor Shapley is among the foremost in these investigations, and he is devising a fairly detailed classification in which new names have to be employed for clearness. He speaks of 'galaxies', 'multiple galaxies', 'super-galaxies', 'the metagalaxy', 'the cosmoplasma'—all systems of bodies within the all-embracing universe. We will not enter into the details of his proposals because, interesting and important though they are, they cannot be regarded as other than a stage on the path to a settled classification. The fact that they exist, however, is an indication of the tremendous new area of inquiry which has been opened up by recent discoveries.

About two million spiral nebulae are within reach of our present telescopes (it should be mentioned, perhaps, that they do not all possess the spiral form and that the more general name, 'extra-galactic nebulae', is preferable, but, important though that is in itself, it is a detail from our present point of view), and this must be only a tiny fraction of the total number in space. The most distant that we can detect is about 140 million light-years away. This raises in our minds the question: how large is space? Unfortunately that is a question which we cannot yet answer. The general laws which have told us that space is finite and that it is expanding give us no data from which to determine the size; that can be obtained only from observation, and at present we have not observed enough. The fact, however, that we can explore so much space as we can makes it worth while to ask whether we can see far enough to detect the expansion of the universe; or, in other words, can our telescopes pierce to distances at which the repulsive force between the various spiral nebulae exceeds their gravitational attraction? If so, nebulae which we observe should be receding from one another and from our stellar system, and the farther apart they are the more rapidly should they be separating. Now we can measure the velocities of many of these objects, and the result of our measurements is that, almost without exception, they are receding from us at very high speeds. The exceptions occur among the nearest of the nebulae, and the speed of recession of the others increases with the distance. Nebulae near the limiting distance which we can reach have been found to be receding at the enormous speed of more than 12,000 miles a second. It is impossible not to claim this fact of observation as direct evidence of the expansion of the universe. It is almost certainly a dissipation of the matter of the universe; our investigation of the general laws of Nature leads us to regard it as due to the expansion of space itself.

If this interpretation is justified we can draw some important conclusions. According to Eddington's calculations the initial radius of space was in that case about 1,200 million light-years. The radius increases rapidly with time, and the rate of increase also becomes more rapid as time goes on, so that the size of the universe now must be very much greater than it was originally. Strangely enough, the data also allow us to estimate the total amount of matter in the universe. It comes to about 10,000 million million million suns. Our own stellar system we have seen to contain about 100,000 million suns, so that this would give the universe a population of 100,000 million stellar systems like ours. Dr. Curtis in 1919, you will remember, estimated the number of spiral nebulae at '100,000 more or less'. By so much has our outlook changed in twelve years!

These figures are beyond imagination, and we must not be too ready to accept them as final. They depend on the assumption that the *whole* of the observed recession of the spiral nebulae is due to the expansion of space. This assumption is not without grave difficulties—it implies that the universe has been in existence for a much shorter time than other lines of evidence indicate. On the other hand, if only part of the observed recession is due to this cause, we are left with an exactly similar effect arising from some cause at present unknown to us. We do not like to invoke unknown causes of phenomena when known ones are ready to hand, but at the same time, in matters concerning the universe it would be the height of folly to suppose that we know of every influence that might be operating. The only wise course is to reserve judgement. We can at least say that our general conclusion that space is expanding is not contradicted, but appears to be supported, by the facts.[1]

It would have been interesting to give some account in this chapter of another great branch of modern research—that concerning the life histories of the stars—but it has not been possible to enter into questions of time; space has claimed all our attention. I think it will be agreed that in the physical sciences, judging from the experience of the last twenty years, peace hath her victories far more renowned than war. May she long continue to achieve them!

[1] Eddington has very recently found it possible to deduce from atomic physics, without any reference to astronomical data, a rate of expansion of the universe which would require the spiral nebulae to recede from one another at the observed rate. This greatly increases the probability that the systematic recession, as observed, is entirely an effect of the expansion of the universe.

Books for Reference

H. Shapley. *Flights from Chaos*. McGraw Hill.
A. S. Eddington. *The Rotation of the Galaxy*. Oxford University Press.
—— *The Expanding Universe*. (To appear shortly in the Proceedings of the Physical Society of London.)
Discussion on 'The Evolution of the Universe'. Supplement to *Nature*. Oct. 24, 1931.

[The summary on page 47 is taken from *The Adolpho Stahl Lectures in Astronomy*, 1919 (Stanford University Press, U.S.A.)]

IV

TENDENCIES IN RECENT ENGLISH LITERATURE

By OSBERT BURDETT

THAT the transition from the slopes of science, the nether slope of the atom and the upper of the furthest star in space, to the real world of poetry may not seem too abrupt, let us begin, with Messrs. Bell's kind permission, with the ode in which Patmore defined the attitude of a poet to both. This poem, which will amuse those who are not enchanted by it, is called *The Two Deserts*, and is to be found, numbered XVIII, in Book I of *The Unknown Eros*:

The Two Deserts

Not greatly moved with awe am I
To learn that we may spy
Five thousand firmaments beyond our own.
The best that 's known
Of the heavenly bodies does them credit small.
View'd close, the Moon's fair ball
Is of ill objects worst,
A corpse in Night's highway, naked, fire-scarr'd, accurst;
And now they tell
That the sun is plainly seen to boil and burst
Too horribly for hell.
So, judging from these two,
As we must do,
The Universe, outside our living Earth,
Was all conceiv'd in the Creator's mirth,
Forecasting at the time Man's spirit deep,
To make dirt cheap.
Put by the telescope!
Better without it man may see,
Stretch'd awful in the hush'd midnight,
The ghost of his eternity.

Give me the nobler glass that swells to the eye
The things which near us lie,
Till Science rapturously hails,
In the minutest water-drop,
A torment of innumerable tails.
These at the least do live.
But rather give
A mind not much to pry
Beyond our royal-fair estate
Betwixt these deserts blank of small and great.

Then comes the beautiful conclusion:

Wonder and beauty our own courtiers are,
Pressing to catch our gaze,
And out of obvious ways
Ne'er wandering far.

By means of this poetic bridge we can pass from science to poetry in order thence to descend into the dusty world of recent English letters. To find our way through the sometimes noisy and always jostling crowd, let us remember that which we are proposing to do: in other words, the limits of the subject.

An attempt to sketch tendencies in present-day literature in England, as a moment's thought will show, must resolve itself into an examination of the work produced in the decade that is just over. Our subject really narrows to literature in the nineteen-twenties. This decade, moreover, had a definite character of its own, for it was a post-war decade, a decade in which the world was staggering under the shock of a huge disaster and was being forced to learn that peace could not be recovered simply by silencing the guns. Further, let us guard against the impression that the War itself was responsible for the confusion afterward. To the historian, no doubt, war is a convenient date for the closing of an epoch; but it is also true, I think, that war is rather the explosion of forces already discernibly at work than the cause of the changes that can be dated from it most conveniently. This, I am sure, is true of the last war. The previous epoch (which we call the Victorian age in England) was already over before the end of King Edward's reign. All that the War accomplished was to give a wider freedom, and to sound a louder note, than would have been given or sounded had the outbreak of 1914 been prevented. It would take us too far back to produce the evidence for this, but no one will deny that the disruption of Victorian standards had been plainly visible at the turn of the century. The novel that contained some of the fiercest criticisms—*The Way of All Flesh*, by Samuel Butler—was published in 1903, and had been actually finished in the 'eighties. Criticism sib to this was vigorous during the succeeding ten years, most conspicuously (to the general public) in the theatre where Bernard Shaw and John Galsworthy had established themselves; and the consequence is that by 1914 definite new tendencies were certain to become prominent even if the War had not given a terrific shock to the world. It may be, therefore, worth while to glance at the situation in 1913 before attempting to describe the immediate delta into which the War turned the rising currents.

A simple reflection will give us one clue. The nineteenth century was dominated by the Romantic movement, and in the history of literature we find that the changes of taste known as the Classical and the Romantic—terms so convenient that they survive all criticism of their value, roughly resolve themselves into alternate cycles of about one hundred years. It was therefore probable that the Romantic movement was nearing its term with the close of the century that it had dominated. The various protests and criticisms making themselves heard between 1900 and 1913 can be conveniently summarized into a reaction against Romance, though it often seemed to be no more than reaction against Victorianism. It was not recognized at once that so stable a society as the Victorian could be

the lap of Romantic ideals; still less, that such a society
is specially apt to give rise to Romantic conceptions; yet,
naturally, Romantic ideals flourish when the background
of life is most secure. Romance blooms like a wild flower in
safe conditions. Then, after it has enjoyed its rise in the
'paradise' of ideals, the ideals become contrasted with the
prosaic reality, and that reality is attacked long before the
ideals themselves are called gravely into question. Thus,
the first phase of a Romantic movement is a phase of
Idealism. Its second phase is a return to the ugly facts on
which Realism seizes, and when the anti- but still allied,
interest of Realism has been exhausted, the order of
society begins to crumble, and in the ensuing transition and
confusion a reaction towards order and authority, that is
toward classical standards, begins to appear. By 1913
Realism had done its work; the Victorian conception of
society was visibly crumbling, and the welter was beginning
that was to end in the explosion of the War.

In England, as it happens, the anti-romantic reaction
was at first more prominent in the plastic arts than in
literature; but it is enough to recall that Vorticism had
reached England in the compositions of Wyndham Lewis
by the summer of 1914. The War provided an apt field,
and became a too perfect excuse, for an attitude of mind
already with us and establishing itself before the first gun
was fired. The exhibition in 1913 of the 'Rock Drill' by
Jacob Epstein proved an almost literal symbol of the
spirit that was to waste Europe for four years. Literature
soon showed the same tendency, and though the 'new
poetry' and the new prose, produced by two groups of
younger writers in manifestoes called 'Wheels' and 'Blast',
were actually published during the War, it is as certain as
anything can be that the War had only an accidental share
in their appearance. If ever there was a living writer
unaffected by war it was Mr. Lytton Strachey, but the
War provided a welcome for his ironic studies of *Eminent*

Victorians, and these appeared in the summer before its end. It was the elderly who were exasperated by his treatment of their heroes. The younger were delighted by it. They found, in his method and approach, a congenial expression of their own impatience with the Victorian past.

These facts are more important than the War or than the Truce to make us understand the mood in which the nineteen-twenties opened, and it must be remembered that the writers who were to break into print between the years 1920 and 1930 had been babies in King Edward's reign, and can be directly connected with the War only in so far as they had fought, or written war-books. The formative part of their experience was post-Victorian, not military. The war-books themselves are in a small and special class apart.

A few dates will help to fix the tendencies discernible.

Mr. T. S. Eliot's *Prufrock* appeared in 1917; Lytton Strachey's *Eminent Victorians* in 1918; and both were congenial to the opening mood of youth in the nineteen-twenties. In 1920 both Proust and psycho-analysis had reached England, and the dramatic success of that year was the revival of *The Beggar's Opera*, which reflected the popular taste for the satisfaction of the animal instincts, for freedom in a world just released from control, for the return of fun, for peace as a holiday. In 1920 also, H. G. Wells's *Outline of History* began to run round a world that had lost faith in everything except hazy scientific surmises; and in 1922 James Joyce published his *Ulysses*, a book in which several sympathetic tendencies were embraced. The nineteen-twenties were the days of the short skirt, the Eton crop, the unregistered marriage, and the decontrolling of concupiscence, when the theatres and the bookshops were filled with a youthful crowd of half-happy, half-restless pleasure-seekers who saw their world without a rudder and were losing faith in everything including themselves. This crowd should take precedence of the books that they devoured and of the old Renaissance and post-Renaissance plays that they were applauding for, as Gautier remarked long ago, ' books follow morals, morals do not follow books. It was the Regency that máde Crébillon, not Crébillon the Regency. The centuries succeed each other, and each bears its own fruit. Books are the fruits of morals.' The year 1922 likewise saw the publication of *The Waste Land*, and in the ensuing decade Virginia Woolf, Aldous Huxley, D. H. Lawrence, André Maurois, Bertrand Russell, and Dean Inge were to make their reputations or, as with the Dean, to extend them by a more popular audience. While the experimenters and the questioners were pursuing their inquiries, the popular taste for freedom continued to rise with the steadily rising skirt (and how lovely that could be!); and the success of Margaret Kennedy's *Constant Nymph* in 1924 was a success given to a novel describing in the fashion of the hour the Bohemian spirit which had found so much delight in the old-fashioned but immortal lyrics of *The Beggar's Opera*.

It would be tiresome to cram a lecture with the names of authors and the titles of books. Therefore, I want you to concentrate on the few just named and to regard each more typically than particularly. Many of these writers are with us still, and some of the changes in their more recent works suggest the tendencies of a later moment. To-day does not become ancient history to-morrow morning, and the nineteen-twenties, please remember, ended but eight months ago [August, 1931]. How are we to group the evidence together? Since, eddying round the tradition still unswamped by the flood of change, a definite spirit seems to be discernible, let us glance at the manifestations of this spirit in poetry, the drama, the novel, biography, and science before endeavouring to peep into the outlook for the 'thirties.

To begin with poetry. In the years before the War, the group most in the general eye was called the Georgians, of

which, upon his death during the War, Rupert Brooke was
the popular chief. These young people had reached the
University or left it but five or six years before the outbreak, and they became known as a group through the
publication of a series of anthologies, edited by Mr. Edward
Marsh, called 'Georgian Poetry'. The title was ingenious,
and the poets gained more reputation from each anthology
than they had gained severally for themselves. This
poetry, as we may see from Rupert Brooke's, was written
in the tradition of Keats and Tennyson. It was graceful,
but it lacked experiment, and hostile critics thought it to
be little more than the cream of magazine-verse. Senior
and outside it, the two best poets of this time, who were
making or had already made their reputations, were Mr.
W. H. Davies and Mr. Walter de la Mare. Davies was and
remains the eternal child, content to stare at birds, and
cows, and flowers, and his *Songs of Joy*, except for the
absence of religious mysticism, form a kind of missing link
between the Elizabethan song books, with a touch, too,
of John Skelton himself, and Blake's *Songs of Innocence*,
as if they had been written by a child of Ballad who had
grown to manhood in Merrie England. They might, from
the 'folk' in them, have been written in any age, and it is
wonderful that such poetry should have survived the
sophistication of our industrial era. But Mr. W. H. Davies
was never schoolmastered! His verse is as refreshing as a
mountain rill, a natural spring, a breath from the hills, and
entirely free from literary sophistication or vulgarity.
Mr. Davies has remained unspoiled, and his simplicity
makes him the most authentic, natural poet now writing
English. Mr. de la Mare is nearer to the magic of Poe and
of Coleridge. Yet, though an elfin music can be heard in
his verse, and he often loves to haunt the borderland of
eeriness and mystery, his range is wider than is often
realized. He has both the horn of elfland and the shep-
herd's pipe, and the child's flute as well. These two true

and original poets both belong to the Romantic tradition, if indeed Mr. Davies does not go further and write poetry barely distinguishable from the babble of a brook or the twitter of the birds. Mr. Edmund Blunden is another poet of Nature, true to that basic inspiration of English verse, and with a personal and particular fondness for fishes. There are as many consonants in his verse as there are pebbles in a brook.

In this, the best poetry of the time, there was no challenge to tradition, and originality seemed rather to refine upon an accepted convention than to show much novelty in form or structure or in the language of poetry. The plastic arts were much more experimental. Poetry remained familiar, and seemed to rebel youth to be asleep.

The anthologies known as 'Blast' and 'Wheels' rudely shattered this repose and revived a fashion for free verse. There has always been, of course, a mixed form between the discontinuous rhythm of prose and the measured and regular rhythm of ordinary poetry. Milton, Cowley, Wordsworth, down to Patmore and Henley have, at times, abandoned the formal pattern and the regular stanza. The experimenters undoubtedly had an irregular tradition behind them; but their anxiety to distinguish themselves from the Georgian group led them to emphasize their departures: to write only in this so-called free verse; to rely upon the printing and alignment to show (not always convincingly) that they were not writing prose; to abandon every conventional epithet; to write poems which should give the abstract pleasure of nursery rhymes or nonsense jingles, and sometimes to be extravagantly silly, affected, unmusical, and dull. The battle over free verse became a free fight, but the free versifiers conquered public bewilderment by pertinacity. Among the best were Edith and Sacheverel Sitwell, who show at times an exquisite ear and generally succeed in convincing us that their odd epithets and calculated unfamiliarities, often of one thing

in terms of another, are rather an escape from the logic of
formally repeated pattern than idle perversities. Once you
have their point of view, you can enjoy their best work
without effort. An immense amount of imitative rubbish
was necessarily written, but the concentration on free
verse was to destroy in the mind of readers the illusion of
the necessity of familiar metrical schemes. This now done,
these poets sometimes return to regular patterns, for verse
which gives the reader little help in finding its melody can
become as tiresome as verse so regular that the reader has
no more to do than when winding up a gramophone or
droning a hurdygurdy. The free versifiers broke the
formality of the stanza, of a regular beat, of mathematically
regular metres and epithets. The substance of poetry they
left little changed, except in one reaction that favoured
ugly subjects. This is worth a word. A dead cat in a pool
might be preferred to a water-lily: because the themes that
had once filled the Realistic novel at length began to have
their counterpart in poems. This is not a detail. It means
that, just as the Realistic novel was really Romance in its
last ditch, so most of the free versifiers were really still
writing at the fag end of the Romantic movement. They
appeared to the public, moreover, to be just as disorderly
in form as had those early Romantic lyrists who broke away
from the couplet, and just as unpoetic in subject as had
the first Romantic poets, their predecessors, when they
wrote songs to Mary and Jane, to a leech-gatherer and to
an idiot boy, instead of to Amaryllis, Chloë, or Lesbia. The
Romantic convention that Tennyson perfected, which had
made Shelley seem the most typical of poets in life and in
lyric, was breaking. Its forms were repudiated; its diction
was ridiculed; its subjects were declared to be exhausted;
but, so far, the poetry had been that of dissatisfied experimenters rather than the definition in poetry of their
own dismay.

Mr. T. S. Eliot's *Love Song of J. Alfred Prufrock*, published in 1917, made no public stir, and some of the poems in it date from 1909; but the volume made friends for him with other young writers and prepared the way for the quiet but steady welcome which greeted *The Waste Land* in 1922. In this lecture I must assume your acquaintance with the poetry mentioned, since there is no time for detailed discussion or illustration of it. We are trying to estimate our apple-crop, not to enjoy the ribstons, the russets, and the pearmains. The title of Mr. Eliot's poem, a beautiful title by the way, is its simplest clue and summary. The end of the Victorian Age in England, indeed in the industrial bogs of all countries, had seen a loss of faith in Christianity with no other belief to take its place. Before the inevitable superstitions, now rampant, had well returned, the Christian virtue of hope had perished, and men tried to fill their void with material interests (in lieu of honour), with the pursuit of knowledge (in despair of wisdom), with private ambitions (in place of unselfish devotion), with restless movement and change (made easy by the motor), with the pursuit of pleasure (made easy by contraceptives), with drift amid the details of existence, but without an end or meaning in their life. It is true that Bergson and his popularizers were essaying a philosophy of evolution, that for many the word evolution itself was not the name of a theory but a talisman to some form of universally true and 'scientific' belief; but this satisfied few and most were suffering from the loneliness of egoism. *The Waste Land* was an apt description of their plight, and Mr. Eliot's other poems dealt with the broken fragments of experience and enjoyed emphasizing their futility. One of his admirers, Mr. I. A. Richards, has said that the poem consists of a 'music of ideas', and to understand its unintelligible medley we are invited to be familiar with a wealth of allusion to obscure, learned, and often arid books. The work can be compared to a broken mosaic, and this broken mosaic is offered to us as a picture

of our minds: a rubbish-heap. The elaborate notes add to
the sense of dreary confusion. The poem is a landmark,
probably a terminus. Despite some of its cadences, it will
never be enjoyed widely for its own sake. Here is verse
that can never be popular. Once its mood is a memory, it
will interest researchers because it will not be easily understood. It will be a quaint bit of evidence. The beauty of
rhythm that its admirers find in it will never be audible to
the general ear, and it shows (I fancy) an imagination
happier in prose. In dread of emotion, its substance is
mainly literary and intellectual. Its favourite device is
an anti-climax of hinted quotations. It has the dry eye of
unsheddable tears. It portrays a sensitive mind in revulsion, disgust, and despair, but so disillusioned that these
strong emotions would be beneath its precarious dignity:
a hint, a shudder, a sneer express its detestation best.
Mr. Eliot comes from New England, and the sensitive
New Englander, having to discover Europe for himself, is
naturally more apt to be disappointed with Europe, to
which he escaped from America, than are we who take it
for granted, and are perhaps less awake to the carious signs
of decay. In *The Waste Land* self-horror likewise was confessed, and the confession was the lancing of a mental
abscess. The younger generation had found a spokesman,
and the piecemeal shape was as welcome to them as the
broken mosaic of its intellectual structure.

Confidence and complacency were Pecksniffian crudities,
and the poetry that Thomas Hardy was writing in his old
age, a poetry in which the deliberately broken rhythms
amplified the disillusioned note, was the only elder poetry
that to the younger experimenters did not seem to date.
His vast dramatic epic *The Dynasts*, dealing with the wars
of a hundred years ago, and substituting an unweeting It
for God was equally welcome. Hardy's attitude to life was
largely the product of Darwinism on a one-time believer
who in his youth very nearly became ordained, who died

sorry that he could not have lived an organist in a country parish. The wonder is that he should have reacted so promptly to implications that became general only forty years later. He did not change. In mood he was forty years ahead of his own contemporaries: the poem called *God's Funeral* is the heart of this dismay.

In all this, two tendencies can be discerned: first a reduction to the fragments of experience; then their analysis; and next a desire to present this (or these) vividly. Hence came the breaking of regular stanzas into little erring rhythms that could be as long or as waylaid and checked as the poet required; then the desire to recover internally design and 'quality', not, of course, in the guise of logical stanzas, but in the texture of the diction itself. The verbal effect was to be a pattern of sound as elaborate inwardly as that of the abandoned exterior stanza. Alexander Pope had spent such a wealth of subtlety upon each line in his couplet that the couplet became transformed. The 'new' poets wished to transform *their* language and to recover by interior subtlety that which the stanza had supplied by exterior rule. By scholarship free verse was to possess the quality of classic order. It is toward that order that poetry tends. Sylvia Townsend Warner's *Opus 7* (note its title) is one illustration of this.

In the theatre, the most commercial and therefore the most laggard of the arts, little happened. There were some attempts at expressionism, but they have remained attempts, praiseworthy in their reaction from an abject naturalism, but little more than an endeavour to short-circuit representation by using symbols or label-like devices. A character would be made to think aloud in the pauses of his normal talk, or a group to echo one another to emphasize that each member had no individuality of his own. Thus 'mass-behaviour' was conveyed by easy imitation. One masterpiece we have had in *The Silver Tassie*, by Mr. Sean O'Casey, whose magnificent play is a rare blend of poetry with realism. This is far more than a war-play. In the second act, which shows the soldiers at the front, poetry and symbolism are used to convey a terribly realistic picture of the front-line; and the chanting of the soldiers in no way diminishes the actuality of the scene, but seems to become the very spirit of mechanical warfare. The author has found a means of using poetry to intensify realism, with the sacrifice of neither and the enhancement of both. The picture is so vivid that only when the first and third acts are contrasted with the chanting of the second do we realize how poetry has been used to make the second the most vivid, but tremendous, of the three. Originality, a drive which goes beyond experiment, created this play, and we may hope that the return of poetry to the stage may be dated from it. Of Bernard Shaw I say little. He is less an artist than a journalist-using-the-stage, and his choice of a religious subject in *Saint Joan* and of a monarchal hero in *The Apple Cart* shows how excellently prompt he is to refract the interests of the moment. The disillusion that culminated in the war was bound to produce some religious reaction; and a woman saint, lately canonized, a woman of action in whom the irreligious could believe, who was moreover a patriot and a soldier, was a knowing choice, and revived the reputation that some had thought to be waning. Similarly, the discontent with parliaments, the recurrence of dictatorships, the increasing, if helpless, dissatisfaction with finance-led industrial capitalism, would probably not have reached the theatre for years if we had not had this great journalist with the gift of turning a discussion of it into dialogue. Mr. Shaw is good at set speeches, good at defining points-of-view, vigorous at argument, but with a very old-fashioned technique of the stage. By the relief provided by little bouts of knockabout farce, and with a dentist's determination, he can make an audience listen to discussions in the theatre. Being equally clever at fixing the limelight on himself, he secures much publicity, and he uses this effectively to focus attention on his work, the interest in which is easily mistaken for a great artistic reputation. Our theatre would be much duller without him, but the conversion of a theatre into a lecture-hall has almost nothing to do with art and very little to do with drama. His style is as mortal as a polished metal machine. When time has corroded it, it will be almost literally a (journalistic) scrap-heap.

Mr. Noel Coward was a genuine discovery of the decade, and his plays, *The Vortex*, *Easy Virtues*, *Fallen Angels*, remain a vivid picture of life in the nineteen-twenties. The people, the morality, were so typical of the post-war world of London, in the class dramatized, that they excited some annoyance, but they were sketched at first-hand by a young man (Mr. Coward was not born until 1899), whose precocious talent naturally revelled in the only world of his experience. It was the survivors, not his contemporaries, who were shocked, and it was the content, not the form, that was arresting. His versatility is great: he is musician, actor, song-writer as well as playwright, but his field is the conventional field of dramatic naturalism, and his originality lies less in creating anything new than in keeping drawing-room drama up to date. His senior, Mr. Somerset Maugham, does the same, only for the already middle-aged section of the audience. Mr. Coward (a boy of only fifteen when the war started) definitely belongs to the post-war world.

One tendency of some credit has been the popularity of the recent historical play, with such heroes as Lincoln, Florence Nightingale, Joan of Arc, or Elizabeth Barrett. The appetite for drama must be in a fairly healthy condition when such plays are popular, for complete banality and travesty would be intolerable in these, and, in these, criticism and indignation would be quick and interested to expose it. Mr. Rudolf Besier's *The Barretts of Wimpole*

Street is an excellent example. Where he goes beyond his evidence and his sources, namely in explaining why Mr. Barrett had such a horror of marriage for his children, he is still credibly in character. The value of the explanation, invention though it be, is to make credible to us a man who, with no more motive than his children knew or than we know from the documents surviving, would remain a stage-monster, which indeed, in his capacity of domestic autocrat, he has seemed for want of any subtler explanation. The new theories of psychology have made us impatient of monsters. We are less anxious to condemn and more anxious to understand. True, the explanation cannot often be agreeable, but the disagreeable has some excuse if light is thrown upon obscure corners by it. *The Barretts of Wimpole Street* is, I think, the best of these recent historical plays, plays which are the drama's part in the recent revival of biography. No one can say whether the series will continue, but it is clear that any competent play upon an historical figure will receive a warm welcome, and little is to be feared from the competition of the bad. Any playwright who can dramatize a standard biography has an opportunity awaiting him. Dramatic lives not yet dramatized are familiar to everybody.

The drama, biography, and to some extent fiction, received an impulse from the Continent that partly explains the new attitude to them. Mr. Strachey's approach in 1918 had been mainly artistic; his method was careful and harmonious selection after the French fashion, and the disillusion of the period, which had seen the rise of Anatole France, necessarily encouraged irony, an irony that would pounce on the little inconsistencies of men. The analysis of the twentieth century succeeded the ideal synthesis of the nineteenth. For a while, we were more interested in the feet of clay than in the golden body of our former idols. But when the theories of Jung and Freud reached England about 1920 they delighted the ironists, because a scientific analysis by mental dissection reduced mankind to a bundle of disgusting appetites, while giving no sanction to the control of these but the necessity imposed by decent society. Why society should desire to be decent was not made very clear to all. Emphasis was, then, thrown upon the indecencies that underlie it. All theories explain something, and the new psychology explained dreams more convincingly than previous surmises, and gave an explanation of prudery which, incidentally, was very diverting to young people who thought prudery the very devil. It encouraged the examination of motives. It argued that impulses should not be dammed. It proposed sublimation. It interpreted the 'good conduct' prizewinner in terms of restraint. Conscience, which can be respected and admired, was called the censor; and what censor has ever been liked? At the same time, apparently by throwing all his emphasis upon it, Proust was reducing life to a stream of consciousness, was exalting reverie, and was isolating the floating background of our minds and thrusting the foreground, of which we had been almost exclusively aware, into the position of an interruption of reverie. This reversal of value was like that former scientific notion which called matter holes in the ether. Thus much combined to push events, action, all conscious life and activity out of the centre of the picture, and to concentrate on the background of the sub-conscious, covert, reflective element in our existence. Memory was dethroning initiative in this work, whence faith and hope had vanished. To explain a character, his chief doings, the things for which he became best known, ceased to suffice. People grew less interested in things than in their explanation, less in the distinction of the great man than in the greatest common factor of him. Instead of asking What did he do? they began to ask two questions: What else did he do? and Why did he do it? His earliest memories now became evidence no less important than his latest deeds.

Thus, the appetite for irony was enforced by a new form of semi-scientific curiosity, and the tone of the former blended very well with the method and conclusions of the latter. Writers and painters—on this theory—once the clue can be applied, are never more self-revealing than when they have been apparently most objective. The analysis of character and motive, and the artistic method of Proust combined with the psychology of Jung to demand a new manner in narrative and in biography.

Of these biographies and novels, the biographies could have one advantage. There is a positive interest in real characters, in men who, having been free from disillusion themselves, retain something of which no analysis or explanation can deprive them. Fiction, on the other hand, usually deals with contemporary life, and there is therefore apt to be no contrast between the mood of the novelist and the mood of his creatures. The world of Mr. Aldous Huxley is a narrow, despairing, and sometimes disgusting world. Futility, despair, indulgence, and consequent disappointment infect these pages like a blight. Nothing remains but a conflict of little egoisms, which the skilful painting alone can redeem. The novels of Virginia Woolf and of Dorothy Richardson are not confined to this narrow gully. Nearer to Proust, but not imitative, they rather try to unravel the consciousness of people who have not abandoned the morals and the beliefs of Christian society. Time is showing that Christian ethics do not long survive the loss of the Christian faith, and the repudiation of Christian morals is an obvious fact in the modern world. The people in Mr. Huxley's stories are men sufficient to themselves, who know nothing but their appetites, and who, in a world empty of everything but egoism, suffer from despair. This takes many forms. Mr. Huxley's characters, having rid themselves of ideas of duty or restraint, may not be happy, but there is no conflict, for their own hesitation has passed. In the novels of D. H. Lawrence,

however, an obsession with sex is seen to be struggling with
the relic of a puritan conscience, and the writer vainly tries
to justify appetites in the vigour of which he believes and
to blame the world for his resentful but ineradicable
suspicion of them. He thinks that he would be healthy if
he could feel himself to be free. That this is an illusion can
be seen in Mr. Huxley's stories. The whole medley has left
a sort of monument to itself in Mr. James Joyce's *Ulysses*,
where a lifetime is reduced to twenty-four hours, where the
details are more conspicuous than the unity, where language
is broken into strata of styles, where decomposition is the
overt purpose and motive. Punctuation was abandoned in
the last chapter; but the attempt was innocent or half-
hearted, for capitals were retained to introduce each
sentence, and, if either be retained, there is no reason to
prefer a capital letter to a full-stop. The innovation certainly emphasized the desultory impressions floating
through the mind of the woman who was supposed to be
day-dreaming in bed, but it was the quality of the writing,
more than the absence of punctuation, that gave the virtue
to this chapter. Experiment in decomposition could not
be carried much further, but in his latest and unfinished
book, some fragments of which have appeared, Mr. Joyce
has succeeded in being more obscure and more incomprehensible.

All this, however, did not monopolize the whole field.
The voice of tradition has not been wanting, and Lawrence
was to end in search of beliefs. Its great achievement in
poetry was *The Testament of Beauty* by the late Poet
Laureate, Robert Bridges. Written in his old age, the
poem was necessarily the testament of one belonging to a
past generation, but the beauty of its verse and the sin-
cerity of its thought make it one of the few good philo-
sophical poems in English. It is a beautiful witness to the
wisdom of the past. It stands out from the mass of contemporary writing by qualities of affirmation; qualities not

only the individual opinions of a man who has discovered them for himself. They are rooted in tradition; they are based upon religion; they have been tested by a long life, and they are not anti-scientific or even reactionary. In style and metre and diction this poem can compare with any modern work without fear, for in all three it is also original; but from despair and disillusion, even on the subject of war, it is free; and, if we contrast the type of mind and character displayed by the poem with the type revealed by (for example) *The Waste Land*, it is impossible to deny that the more traditional is the healthier. Some of the modernists referred to its reception in grudging terms. Bridges could not help that ephemeral 'success'. Where this grudge was not revulsion from immediate popularity, it confessed, perhaps, the rebuke that all affirmation gives to a hollow scepticism.

This scepticism is reflected credulously in the great popularity of recent books on science, such as those (which you probably know also, or through translations) by men like Eddington and Jeans, and through the writings of popularizers such as Mr. H. G. Wells. The scientists deal with immediate, verifiable knowledge, whereas religion, a system of faith and worship, is less concerned with the phenomenal than with the transcendental. All that has happened is that the methods of applied science occupy public attention to the exclusion of other testimony to truth, and people are now as credulous of anything that can be called scientific as they ever were of non-scientific myth or miracle. If, therefore, we wish to see the inferences based on current science criticized, we have to turn to men of religion, and the most vigorous of these critics is Mr. Hilaire Belloc. It is always stimulating to read some one unaffected by the fashion of his time, and among the mass of his writings do not overlook two books of lively controversy. One, called *Survivals and New Arrivals*, under which he grouped the enemies of the Roman Catholic faith, was published in 1929. The other, called *Essays of a Catholic*, was issued in July 1931, a few days before I left England. Mr. Belloc writes extremely well. At his best he is a master of fine prose, whether descriptive, argumentative, or expository. He is never afraid to say what he thinks, or to give the reasons for his thinking. He is sincere enough to see the advantage that comes from a direct challenge, from pushing vigorously *against* the current of opinion, of arousing his readers to the philosophy implicit in many of the notions they have lazily assumed, of making them think by examining an assumption that they have thoughtlessly taken for granted, of questioning the assertions of an author whose success or prestige has sent them to sleep. In these two books—which may be overlooked because we prefer silence to argument in England—whatever your own response may be, you will find a brilliant summary of many tendencies in current literature.

There appears another tendency: the stiffening of traditional opposition to the anti-Christian morals, to industrialism, scepticism, and to the rebellions of the past decade. There is a definite, if minority, move toward the Right, and a classical reaction toward authority and control is discernible. Mr. T. S. Eliot, who has joined the Anglo-Catholic section of the Church of England, is now writing religious verse, and Miss Sitwell has written an enthusiastic study of Alexander Pope. In other words the notes of challenge and adventure are passing from the Romantic to the Classical camp, and initiative has returned to the latter. We shall not see any reaction all along the line; but the Romantic tide is no longer at the flow, and classical eddies will be more confident and more numerous. Meantime, there is always a place for sincere and honest work, work that seems to belong to no school or tendency, but in which can be discerned 'the easy path so hard to find' by the champions of either party. With two examples, one in prose and one in verse, I will conclude.

Mrs. Edward Thomas, the wife of the poet who was killed in 1915, has written a very moving account of her engagement and her marriage in a pair of volumes called *As it Was* and *World Without End*. Their candour would have made them impossible before the Victorian taboos were broken, but a simplicity and a tragic beauty inform her narrative. It is a book to contrast with the unlike, but not very dissimilar, story of Gaudia-Brescka's life: *Savage Messiah*.

The other is much stranger. The *Poems* of Gerard Manley Hopkins, first published (twenty-eight years after his death) by the late Poet Laureate in 1918, have lately been reprinted, and his life was published in 1930. There is time to mention only two things about them. The verse was so experimental that it could not be published in the only magazines open to the author while he lived, for he was a Jesuit, occupied in teaching, and an author only in his odd hours. Beside the strange experiments in metre, a scholarly diction and a difficult style, looking like free verse but actually composed in a set of deliberately varied metres, the beauty of this poetry is unmistakable. The reader seems to have been drenched from a sudden, secret spring. Thus Hopkins, who was writing (unknown to all but a few friends like Robert Bridges) in the 'seventies and 'eighties, was as experimental as the most adventurous of forty years later, and at the same time achieved a beauty that no obscurity can hide. His fame has grown slowly, and will continue to grow; but it shows that the Romantic convention was not exhausted and had created new and original forms, unknown to the world, even before Tennyson's death in 1892. Whether in experiment or beauty, Hopkins easily rivals his successors, and the very late appearance of his poetry invites comparison with theirs.

This sketch of recent and current tendencies is as bald, I fear, as any diagram must be. The kind of substance, the gender of form, is a dry classification, while the life of this literature needs quotations, and better still, experience of itself. Of the future it is rash to say anything, but it would be timid not to speak at all. While the wheat and the tares will continue to jostle each other, readers like writers will be subject to change. Our clothes suggest one tendency. Feminine stockings are returning; feminine sleeves are returning. What does this mean? Think of 1830. The skirt always lengthens with the lengthening days of peace, and the younger among us (if peace endures) may live long enough to witness the resurrection of the tiresome Mrs. Grundy.

The subject has produced some studies, of which here are four:

Tradition and Experiment; by various, and typical, authors. Oxford University Press, 1929.

Edwin Muir. *Transition*. Hogarth Press, 1926.

A. C. Ward. *The Nineteen-Twenties*. Methuen, 1930.

Harold Nicolson. *The New Spirit in Literature*. B.B.C. pamphlet (Sept. 1931): a marvel for fourpence.

THE TOWN HALL, STOCKHOLM

V

SOME TENDENCIES IN SWEDISH ARCHITECTURE

By RAGNAR ÖSTBERG

THE mighty graves on the Upsala plain in Sweden had already stood there for many centuries, when, a thousand years ago, Olof Skötkonung, the Swedish king, had himself baptized at Husaby field; whereupon the sacrificial feasts at the heathen temple of Upsala came almost entirely to an end.

The Upsala barrows, those mighty mounds which enclose the last resting-places of our olden kings before the Middle Ages, still bear witness to heathen power of creation and to gigantic power. Like mighty mountain ridges they lift themselves towards the sky and break the monotony of the wide plain. Like dull, heavy tombs they force themselves up from another world, rolling like mighty waves of sounding memories.

Not far from these barrows there still stood in the eleventh century our mighty heathen temple, untouched, and in use; built of great blocks of dark granite, with its interior adorned by sheets of gold. There, in the temple, sacrifices were made to the old gods, Odin, Tor, and Frej, while outside, the tree-tops of the holy grove sighed round the temple. It was St. Erik, the patron saint of Stockholm, who broke the heathen customs and with them the heathen temple-walls. On the old foundations he built up that Christian medieval church which to-day rises between the barrows. As in former days the building monuments of heathendom and Christian Middle Ages still melt together.

Very near the site of Upsala and its university they form together the greatest memorial of Sweden's ancient days.

The primeval peasant culture which existed in Sweden centuries before the introduction of Christianity now made way, slowly, for the culture of the Latin race, which, together with Catholicism, came into the country during the later Middle Ages. Catholic churches, indeed, were being built in different parts of Sweden (in Västergötland, in Sigtuna, and on Gotland), while sacrifices were still offered to the old gods in the temple at Upsala. These Christian churches were built of stone, a material which at that time was seldom employed in Sweden. The dense forests of the country led to the most solid constructions being built of timber, both peasants' farms and the mansions of great landowners being generally constructed of heavy logs of timber.

The churches, too, were often constructed of wood, and the stones ordinarily occurring in Sweden—granite, limestone, and sandstone—were but seldom employed.

In Gotland, however, there was developed—partly in consequence of the extensive commercial connexions of that island, partly in consequence of its calm, secluded position and its wealth of sandstone and limestone—as early as during the beginning of the Middle Ages a vigorous ecclesiastical architecture, with stone as the material, which even to-day, in hundreds of small country churches, bears witness to a peculiar Romanesque and Gothic architecture of northern character. These buildings have the easy access to easily worked stone to thank for their wealth of artistic details and an ornamental execution, which otherwise was seldom found in the coarsely fashioned buildings on the Swedish mainland. Individual farmyards, still standing here and there and still inhabited, also bear witness to an ancient building-style, in timber, with thatched roofs. Their low-lying masses expand and press themselves like barrows to the earth, and the lines of the buildings are of special interest when they are compared with these monumental mounds. The round, flat-form, intimately connected with the ground, is common to them both, a characteristic feature in the planning which can also be recognized in our old Swedish 'round churches' of granite from that period.

These Romanesque buildings (erected in little populated and remote tracts), as well as the country churches of later date, with their simple forms and their Gothic arches, served—with their granite walls often two yards thick and their fortified towers—not only for divine service but also as positions of defence.

Erected by the inhabitants of the district, often under the direction of builder-monks, these erections (for example, Varnhem Church in Västergötland) have an original and national character. National, too, are the Gothic cathedrals at Upsala, Skara, Linköping, &c., erected, at a later date, of stone. Simultaneously bricks began to come more and more into use, thus giving rise to a kind of Swedish building renaissance.

Under the influence of the royal liberator, Gustavus Vasa, in the sixteenth century, the most important epoch in Swedish architecture develops at the same time that he, as king, laid the political and religious foundations of the whole kingdom. With a natural sense for simplicity and solidity in buildings he directed, often with his own hands, many building enterprises in the country. The most magnificent of these is Vadstena Castle. Originally built after a plan recalling earlier French castles, there still remain the main building, the corner towers, and the moat, with the castle courtyard lying behind, with its compact masses, its immense, yet quiet proportions and its interesting window-grouping in which respect was paid to the demand made by the renaissance for elaborate regularity. This castle at Vadstena remains a monument of pure Swedish architecture. The inner rooms, too, with their enormous measurements—being often more than eleven yards broad —and with ceilings of straight massive beams, bear witness to the heavy solid vigour of our sixteenth century.

G

The castles of Upsala, of Gripsholm, and of Kalmar, which are built of bricks, are distinguished by the same monumental and simple but solid architectural art.

During the seventeenth century and, more especially, during the eighteenth, we trace more evident influences from the south. The cause of this is to be found in the lively communications with the rest of Europe kept up by Sweden during its time of great power after the Thirty Years' War.

The calm and massive forms are still found, it is true, and to a certain extent the severity—for example at Tidö Castle and the magnificently situated Läckö Castle—but the solid material and the solid execution are not noticeable to the same degree. The walls are often built with a mixture of brick and granite and the faces are finished off with mortar. This tendency to decoration and somewhat southern European ornament attains its full development during the eighteenth century, more immediately as a result of the Italian training of the great Swedish architects, Tessin the elder and Tessin the younger. In the case of the former, Tessin the elder, however, we can still see in his stiffer forms his inheritance from the Vasa period —for example, in his Axel Oxenstiernas Palace lying opposite St. Nicholas' Church in Stockholm (Storkyrkan). Tessin the younger, on the other hand, always allows his Italian taste to exercise its influence. It is only in his masterly and imposing masses that one can still trace a strongly Swedish characteristic. His royal palace at Stockholm (occupying an area of 30,000 square metres) with its regular symmetry, its rich divisioning by many pilasters, its dressed walls, and its elegant proportions, constituted for more than a century a determining form for Swedish architecture, just as his decorative tone and his Italian room-creations lived long under French influence. The Carolean chapel in Riddarholm Church, Stockholm, is a magnificent example of the monumental art of the two

Tessins, while, at the same time, it allows us to feel a slight breeze from the rococo period.

The cosmopolitan character of the nineteenth century brought about in Sweden in a higher degree, perhaps, than in any other cultural country, that mixture of various historical architectural styles—from the Greek and the Renaissance down to those of the Middle Ages and the baroque—which, of course, is everywhere based on academic instruction, just as much as it is on an actual feeling for living architecture.

In Sweden, as in many other countries at that period, the superabundance of foreign study material prevented a formation of a style with harmonious national character. That this weakness of character—especially when it is a question of such a branch of art as architecture determined by climatical and local conditions—constituted a danger was seen clearly enough during the last decade of the nineteenth century.

It has, therefore, been the endeavour of Swedish architects during the present century to bring about a more technically perfected, modern architecture which shall be based on a study of our national monumental buildings.

After all the eclectic form of architecture which was in vogue in Sweden, as in the rest of the world during the nineteenth century, there followed at the close of that century and ever since 1900, among Swedish architects, a very strong and extremely youthful enthusiastic movement to escape from foreign *motifs* and to obtain inspiration entirely from native and original sources. This movement was in connexion with, and was in many respects the result of, that poetry—both prose and verse—which formerly and simultaneously flourished in Sweden and which was represented by such northern authors as Ibsen, Strindberg, and Heidenstam. Their permeating demand

for truth, their impulsive criticism of the existing state of
society, their strong stressing of the individual, and their
artistically superior and original form-creation impressed
Swedish consciousness in a very high degree, and essentially
influenced artistic opinion as a whole. This, not least, in
that group of architects who, at the beginning of the
present century, took the lead in their art in Sweden. In
them the demand for truth assumed the form of a desire
for the use of genuine material, to be exhibited such as it
really is, whether in stone, in brick, or in façade-treatment.
There arose also a desire to allow the determining constructions and the individual purposes to reflect their
essential details as faithfully as possible in volume-
development and in external mass-formation.

The intensively critical temperament of the poets was,
in the case of the architects, displayed in a suspicion of the
prevalent and slavish repetition of old established styles.
The poets' stressing of individual values led to endeavours
to discover a personal expression, however simple it might
be, if merely there could be traced in it no borrowed ideas.
Finally, the artistic, all-permeating atmosphere awakened
in the architects a desire for great features, in unity with
nature and with surroundings. A more eloquent creation
of details appeared in the same time.

No long time passed before this individual sense began
to seek for its root, to seek for a trunk around which it
could cling—and found it. The architects discovered that,
as a matter of fact, this root was close at hand in austere
works from long vanished times; in their own so much
decried country. A most earnestly pursued labour now
began in the study of these works in town and in country,
with an eye attentive to see, not least, how these forms had
been set amid the surroundings, and how these forms co-
opatered with adjacent buildings; to observe the simple
main ideas and the unaffected natural growth where, it is
true, the robust is often striking, but where too, on the

other hand, the tenderly cared-for details become of still greater effect.

As a result of these studies there followed the publication of a series of illustrated volumes, among others *Gamla Svenska Städer* ('Old Swedish Towns'), edited by an association of architects and art-historians, and at the reorganized High School of Art there was established a special professor's chair in Swedish architecture in which, among other details, the architect pupils had the obligation—but a most welcome one—to take part every year in the work of measuring important old Swedish buildings. The result of this work, which still continues, is published yearly under the title of *Swedish Architecture, the Architectural Memorials Association.* These uniform studies, under the guidance of the teachers, have undoubtedly contributed in the highest degree to a concentrated work on a common, fundamental tone.

It was especially the buildings from the sixteenth century, already referred to, from the Gustavus Vasa period, which attracted the first initiators of this work of adjustment and which, to a certain degree, in its fundamental principles, became predominant in several of the works which they created. But as, simultaneously, the sentiments already mentioned, which were in unison with those of our poets, had a living import and made their influence strongly felt, these new buildings were characterized by their appropriateness and by their material detail, the rhythm and imagination of the characteristic features of their own times.

The materials which in a special degree captivated this epoch were brick and granite. Doubtless these materials, just like limestone, had been richly employed by the immediate predecessors of the new architects, but then with less respect paid to the special character of the material itself and rather with attention to their ability to receive the forms, whatever they happened to be, which were

dictated by the building style employed. In a word, they
played a relatively dead role as material, and were compelled merely to constitute an unimportant link in the
general form-creation, or to serve refreshingly, by the mere
contrast of colour-effects.

When brick was now subjected to a new treatment, a
beginning was made by investigating with great exactness
the technique of the manufacture of the bricks at the
brick-works. Here were discovered perfectly undreamed
possibilities of giving new life to this material: the old,
machine-pressed, smoothed, even bricks—absolutely the
same in colour in each stone, and for all the bricks in respect to each other—were exchanged for hand-made bricks,
with a treatment in the kilns, which gave an altogether
different result: where every brick with its definite measures
obtained a certain robust surface in shifting values of the
same fundamental tone, a dull red colour, where the placing
in the kiln often allowed the creation of shades approaching
black. Afterwards, in their employment in the façade-wall,
there was often adopted the so-called 'monk-bond'. But,
above all, there was observed the weighty importance for
the effect of the façade-surface that dwelt in the very joint-
measurements, and in which an important part was played
by the treatment of the mortar-joints. In this way one and
the same brick could, in a length of façade-surface, give
altogether varying effects. Generally speaking, I should
like to say that the pointing entirely determines the effect
of the brickwork, and that the most varying expressions,
both in the form of relief, or of altogether differing colour-
values on the façade as a whole, can be obtained if attention be properly directed to the jointing itself. By the
employment, for example, of horizontal broad joints of a
different measure to the perpendicular thinner and more
pressed joints, by the more robust or finer treatment of
the very mortar: by the colouring of the mortar itself, &c.
Of course, all these are things that are well known, but

they are things which at all events were embraced by us
with all the pleasure given by a discovery, so little had
they been employed by our predecessors and so richly did
they give an opportunity of allowing the material itself—
and not the form only—to speak out.

In the same way, the treatment of the hewn stone was
begun in the very stone-mason's yard, in co-operation with
the workmen, and by this means there were obtained,
especially when it was the question of granite, which is
so abundant in Sweden, constructions, methods of hewing
and of treatment, which allowed this strong stone to speak
its altogether characteristic language, and it was placed in
the brickwork only where its native strength could make
itself effective. One constant feature, consequently, was
that while one, it is true, always coerced a material, this
was done within the natural limits determined by the
material in question. It was allowed to play in the or-
chestra in its own special way, and it shone there in that
form-harmony dictated by the architectonic composition
as a whole. This, of course, is nothing new: that is best
known to us here, but it was a utilization of, and a devotion
to, an ancient and well-tested truth, which was new and
life-giving for us because it had so long been neglected, and
because we ourselves had made the discovery; for, as we
must all admit, there is no joy equal to that of the in-
ventor. We may call it, if you like, the naïve belief that
one did discover, but this naïve pleasure was felt in the
midst of all our efforts. Liberation from the slavish following of form-creations was felt by us as an immense
relief, and the longing to be free—in spite of all the necessary restrictions—led to a closer investigation of what was
meant by compulsion, and to a different appreciation of
what really was necessary.

The really weighty and lasting values in that undeniable
striving for originality which lay in the demand for in-
dependence of these first years were, undeniably, in the

first place, to recognize the necessity for a new building to be at one with its surroundings. The weighty and, perhaps, the most important fact was that architecture became for us a room-creating art. Here, too, we imagined we made discoveries, because the workers of the previous half-century had sinned so deeply in this respect. Each building was then looked upon as a totally independent unit and, in the interiors, the room-volume disappeared as a consequence of the mass of architectonic and decorative elements employed there, and which often altogether killed the room as such, killed expanse-effect, and the values of surfaces. How did we not admire the ability of ancient buildings to sink into the landscape; to fade into it; or in the little old towns, to see how the streets, so to say, formed but one whole, and how the individual buildings seemed to chat amicably with their neighbours. Out of all this there grew a feeling of *milieu* which became a fundamental tone in our compositions, and which, quite naturally, afterwards gave birth to the world of *motifs* in which we moved.

This need of a *milieu* which could be felt as a unity, in combination with the clear view of architecture as being first and foremost a room-creating art, gave rise, too, to special care being devoted to the treatment of the courtyards in the building-plan. Here it was possible for oneself to determine one's *milieu* (which otherwise was not a very attractive task): here one could create the great open room for which one so longed with a free and constantly varying expanse as a magnificent background. The courtyard, formerly so neglected, now became a delightful refuge for the architect's right of self-determination, and for a sense of completeness, undisturbed by interferences from the many varying wills of the times. The courtyard became a new discovery and, as a matter of fact, gave quite new values to the interior life of the building—new values at least in the North, for we know well of what importance

THE BLUE HALL, STOCKHOLM TOWN HALL

and beauty the courtyard-constructions are in the south of
Europe.

The room-sensation extended, however, until it became
an important factor in the creation of the entire interior
of a building. It was no longer a question of the forming
of the main mass and the façades, but our planning also
embraced the importance of the special creation of each
room in regard to plan and volume and, when the purpose
and effect so demanded, also to the relative proportions
between the rooms. Perhaps it is right in this case to emphasize the creation of expanse-effect, while restraining the
decorative element in the shaping of the rooms, as being
things of subordinate value: this is the chief characteristic
of modern Swedish architecture. At all events the solution
of these room-problems is for us architects a most attractive
and interesting problem, and I both believe and know that
a successful result in this respect has a noteworthy capacity
to speak to, and be enjoyed—just like a melody—by a
great number of people of widely different classes. Room-
creation brings people nearer to each other; it embraces
them, and it is real power in the hands of architects. All
this, of course, we know very well from the architecture of
great epochs—but it should be remembered more frequently in everyday work than has hitherto been the case
in modern times.

VI

THE PRESENT POSITION IN BIOLOGY

By DORIS MACKINNON

BIOLOGY is the study of life in all its manifestations; but as living organisms group themselves into two main categories, plants on the one hand and animals on the other, and as no man, however curious or industrious, can hope at the present day to learn more than a fraction of what is known concerning either group, it seems inevitable that most biologists should be primarily either botanists or zoologists. It happens that I am concerned with the study of animal life, so you will forgive me if, in speaking of the present position in biology, I seem to stress the zoological aspect.

In the midst of all our learning and our teaching there are moments when we pause to draw breath, and at such moments we try to take stock of what is happening: we try to estimate the tendencies of our times: we become, in a small way, historians. While thus drawing breath, I have been looking back over the last ten years, and I have searched for some clue to what has animated the research and, indirectly, the teaching in biology since the War came to put its paralysing check for a time on all scientific work that had not a direct application to the problems facing the belligerents in Europe.

If I had been speaking sixty years ago, I should have had something more dramatic to announce than I can tell you of to-day. In the latter half of the nineteenth century, when the Darwinian theories were establishing themselves, there was an outburst of activity among biologists, and the science of biology drew to its study many of the best minds. For suddenly, under the touch of that magic wand, the doctrine of organic evolution, to which Darwin's theory of natural selection was mainly instrumental in giving

its rightful power over men's thoughts, the scattered facts
accumulated for long years by the systematists, the em-
bryologists, the anatomists, and the palaeontologists, began
to sort themselves, to recombine, to move into their rightful perspective, and, for the first time, to 'make sense'.
The stimulus given by the new outlook on biological fact
lasted until nearly the end of the nineteenth century; then
it seemed that the possibilities had temporarily been exploited, and a period of some stagnation set in. The inevitable happened; biologists specialized more and more on
minor problems, and each group was little interested in the
work of the others. There were the comparative anatomists
(the zoologists proper, so to speak) mainly concerned with
the study of structure as such; and there were the physiolo-
gists, dealing chiefly with function in the human body and
with what could be gleaned of illuminating comparisons
based on the study of a few 'laboratory animals' such as
guinea-pigs and frogs. At the end of last century there was
still a good deal of life in physiological investigation, since
there seems to be no limit to the experiments you can perform if you are ingenious and curious, and since the outcome of such work has such an obvious bearing on medicine. But the anatomists appeared to be coming to the end
of what they could do to bring fresh evidence in support
of the doctrine that had inspired their recent studies.
There were, of course, many people for whom the recording
of new species was an important event, and many more
to whom the working out of phylogenetic trees gave
infinite scope for their ingenuity and their imagination.
But it was significant that, in the early dawn of this
twentieth century, the race of great biologists seemed to be
passing: the divorce between the study of structure and the
study of function, the neglect of the study of life *as a
whole*, had made the appeal of biology less real: there was
no longer material sufficiently stimulating to make demands on the first-class mind, and so increasingly men with

scientific inclinations turned their attention towards the study of physics and of chemistry, where new and stimulating theories were opening up fresh fields to conquer.

But already before 1914 there were signs that a change was imminent. The stagnant waters of biology were troubled by the heretical activities of a few discontented persons who maintained that, after all, biology is the study of life and not merely of the bodies, animals, and plants that are dead. It was whispered that in the seventeenth and eighteenth centuries zoologists were also botanists, and that they studied the habits of animals as well as their skeletons and viscera. The mysteries of ontogeny might have more than merely 'recapitulatory' value. The geneticist lifted up his voice. The palaeontologist produced disconcerting evidence that the genealogical trees of the comparative anatomist required much drastic pruning. A new spirit of inquiry breathed on the waters.

Then came the War, and all that that implied of loss to science. I speak not only of the lives of men, though there were many killed in those four years who would have been leaders in a new biological advance if they had not fallen in battle. But inevitably those four years were relatively very barren in research. America and the neutrals went their way for a time, but the effort was half-hearted: you cannot sit with one eye on the microscope and the other focused on the trenches. Actually, of course, in the hospitals many things of biological interest were learnt by the way—concerning epidemic disease and prophylactic measures, for instance, and concerning the comparative resistance of shell-shocked and of healthy human tissues. The study of morbid psychology on a vast number of subjects taught something to our doctors and to our lawyers, for which all overstrained civilians have since had cause to be thankful. There were a few biologists serving in the armies during the War who employed their leisure in strange countries to study animal life. But these instances were relatively few. For four long years the majority of biologists, like other people, shot one another, or made shells, or bound up one another's wounds.

And now that for twelve years we have once more been at peace, what is there to record? There has been a great change, but it has come imperceptibly: the signs of its coming were already evident some years before the War, and I regard it still as merely the preliminary to a new apprehension of the study of life. I ask myself whether there is anything in the psychology of the present generation of mature men and women that is especially characteristic of our age? Is there anything there that will help to explain the change of which I am to speak? Anything for which the War itself, and the ghastly aftermath of the War, may not in some degree be actually responsible? Someone said the other day that the men of the twentieth century differ from their forefathers chiefly in their heightened sensibility. This development is obvious enough in our literature, I consider; but I maintain that it is manifest also in our scientific work.

The biologist returned to his laboratory profoundly disheartened, profoundly sceptical concerning much that the nineteenth century had taught him to regard as fact, but also sensitive to many new aspects of life. I find that the attitude of the modern biologist of the more promising sort is a curious mixture of disbelief, expectancy, and hope. He is at once more daring than his predecessors and more timid than they; he is readier than they to acknowledge that the study of life as a whole is his province, but he is overwhelmed by the responsibility that increase of knowledge on so many sides has brought on him; and he is vastly more sensitive to interrelations and interdependences, not only between the various aspects of biology, and between biology and other sciences, but also between the organisms with which he has to deal, and between the several parts of these organisms, which parts, for convenience sake, but to the detriment of a study of life, the later Victorians studied as separate things.

If the War has taught us nothing else, it has taught us that you cannot take a part from a living whole and the remainder continue unchanged and healthy.

It is becoming clear that if biologists are to penetrate further into life's mysteries they must join forces with workers in other branches of knowledge. Team-work between biologists and chemists is coming more and more into vogue; increasingly the biologist consults the physicist and the mathematician, and he is even prepared to give some attention to the criticisms that the philosophers level against his crudities.

A young biologist recently defined the living organism as 'an event, i.e. a spatio-temporal entity having a certain stability of character which is recognizable as one persistent thing or perceptual object', and he went on to state that it is characteristic of the organism 'that the pattern which characterizes a given slice of the event which is its situation is not repeated in every slice'. The writer considered that the lamentable separation between the study of structure and the study of function 'rests largely on the separation between space and time'.

I submit that the framing of such a criticism by a biologist would have been impossible a few years ago. I refer to it here as symptomatic of a growing dissatisfaction among the younger biologists with outworn definitions, and as a hopeful sign that some of them are trying to meet the demands of the modern philosopher, who, for his part, has been influenced by the recent discoveries in physical science.

A great deal of the modern biologist's energy is devoted to investigation of problems connected with what in a general way is called 'genetics'. A special terminology has inevitably grown up around this subject, and the published work of most geneticists is almost unreadable by the non-expert. This is a pity, since the layman is vitally interested in the question of heredity and is eager to learn anything that seems to have direct bearing on certain human problems.

The work of Weismann and his followers in the nineteenth century established for most biologists the fact that an animal or a plant tends to resemble its parents more than it resembles other organisms, because it is actually made from a portion of the same germinal material that gave them shape. Just how far this germinal material is sheltered from outside influences, just how far it can be modified by happenings in the life of the parents within whose bodies it lies concealed—these questions are still discussed; but, in spite of the experimental evidence recently brought by Kammerer, Harrison and others, the belief among biologists is general that the inheritance of acquired characters does not normally occur.

Since the child is, in most cases, the offspring of two parents, and since its body is built up from equal germ-plasm contributions from those two, it should show a mixture of their characteristics and so should be, in a sense, a 'new' creature. Sometimes, however, the characters inherited from one parent are ascendant over corresponding characters inherited from the other, and the child may seemingly be more the child of its father than of its mother. But within that child's body both contributions are there in equal part, even though imperfectly expressed; and the silent characteristics may reappear in subsequent generations when the masking effect of the dominant strain is removed. The laws of Mendel, first formulated in 1866 and revived in the early years of this century by Bateson and De Vries, have played a great part in all recent work on this and allied problems. Certain short-lived organisms, particularly suitable for laboratory breeding, have been exhaustively studied, and the accuracy with which the results of mating one fruit-fly of known lineage with another whose past history has also been analysed are now, thanks to the intensive experiments of Morgan and his school, predictable with something like mathematical certainty. And this in regard to some 400 characters displayed by the adult insect. The fruit-fly is useful experimental material, since it breeds every ten days and produces several hundred offspring in each generation. But we are learning a great deal also, though more slowly, concerning the outcome of mating certain varieties of relatively slow-breeding vertebrate animals together. We are learning how to produce new and stable varieties of domestic animals, combining two or more desirable characters occurring separately in the parent stocks. The future value of such work from the practical standpoint can scarcely be overestimated. The geneticist should be given a free hand with his experiments, for even if it takes him many years to establish the desired type, a method based on scientific principles is ultimately much less expensive than the hit-and-miss procedure of the old breeders. His success with plants of economic value has already justified all the time and thought and money that have gone to the establishment of the new varieties. The case with animals is more difficult, once you get away from comparatively simple characters like coat-colour, comb-shape, and so forth. For characters of economic value in animals, such as milk-yield in cattle and egg-laying capacity in fowls, are apparently dependent on the harmonious co-operation of a number of different factors. The geneticist is confident that he *can* obtain the desired results if he is given time and freedom for experimentation. He is convinced that the same biological laws hold true for cattle and poultry as for fruit-flies, wheat, and potatoes. And he believes that even on the still more subtle questions affecting the inheritance of desirable human qualities, or, equally important, the elimination in human stocks of what is socially undesirable, he will eventually be able to give sound practical advice. But he is still at the beginning of his task.

There can be no question as to the reality of the observed genetical phenomena. The experiments have been repeated again and again. Any breeder with the necessary knowledge and the necessary patience can reproduce the results and confirm them. It really does seem legitimate to consider the organism from this point of view as a sort of mosaic, and to assume that for every character there are paired counterpart factors, or 'genes', in the germ-cells, which somehow segregate when the germ-cells ripen, and in such a way that each egg and each sperm is 'pure' for the character in question; and when the germ-cells, male and female, meet at fertilization they unite to give a new creature that combines in its constitutional make-up duplicate factors for any particular character, or else a contradictory pair, only one of which may find expression if the phenomenon of dominance happens to be involved.

Now I do not pretend that there is anything immediately 'new' in these discoveries. Knowledge that the factors determine heritable characters segregate in the germ-cells as these develop and recombine in predictable ratios in the succeeding generations has been the basis of most of the genetical work in the last thirty years. But what I think is new is our increasing awareness of interdependences between the factors. Separate gene pairs are split, shuffled, and dealt independently of one another—that has long been known. But unless you get the factor for black hair dealt out along with the factor for the expression of pigmentation you will not get a black-haired animal. And where the colour of the human skin is in question—with all that this involves in race-colour questions—it seems that the genes bringing in pigmentation may be of multiple character; which at once complicates the inquiry. It also appears that a double dose of certain factors may prove dangerous to the organism as a whole. And we have also discovered that certain factors are definitely 'linked', and that they tend to pass over or to segregate together.

H

There is a very general belief among geneticists that sex
is a character heritable in much the same way as eye-
colour is heritable in certain animals, such as the fruit-fly.
And here we come to what is still the debateable ground
in the more theoretical aspect of the subject of genetics.
Probably most biologists would not admit that there is
still occasion for debate. For it is generally believed that
the heritable characters of an organism have their material
determinants, factors, or genes resident in definite structures, the chromosomes—discrete bodies into which the
staining material, the chromatin, of the nucleus of the
germ-cells, as of all the body-cells, condenses when the
egg or sperm mother-cells mature and divide. The chromatin of the nucleus is held to be the physical basis of
heredity. It would take me too long to lay before you now
the evidence on which this belief is based; moreover, much
of the work belongs to the pre-War period and so is outside
the range of this chapter. A vast 'literature' has been built
on the subject. Biologists who believe that the chromosomes bear the factors for the hereditary qualities—and
these biologists are the great majority—are prepared to
demonstrate that the factors, or genes, have a linear arrangement on the chromosomes and a definite situation there in
respect of one another. They also claim that factors within
certain chromosomes recognizable under the microscope
determine whether an animal or a plant will bear ova or
spermatozoa, just as certain others will determine whether
it will have blue eyes or brown. In the fruit-fly the organisms
with what is called a double X chromosomal constitution
are females, whereas those with the chromosomal constitution XY are males. A comparable state of things holds
in the cytology of certain other animals whose germ-cells
have been studied. But while it may be true that such a
chromosomal make-up is characteristic of one sex or the
other, some biologists still object that these phenomena are
not necessarily any true index that the 'cause' of sex, or

of any other somatic character, is necessarily resident in the chromosomes. The chromosomal make-up of an animal or a plant may be no more than the visible expression, convenient enough for the geneticist, of something still more remote and subtle in the constitution of the living substance, protoplasm, of which the chromatin is merely a specialized portion.

On the chromosome theory, the sex of an organism should be determined once for all from the moment the sperm from the father meets the egg from the mother. But we know that sex is reversible in many animals, and apparently without there being any corresponding upset of their chromosomal apparatus. We actually find that an animal with a chromosomal constitution that should make it a male may switch over, through a period of hermaphroditism, to a condition in which it is a female. To account for this and many other strange phenomena various ingenious modifications of the sex-chromosomes theory have become fashionable. It is now suggested that certain sex-determining substances are liberated by the gene resident in the sex-chromosomes, perhaps also in the other chromosomes, and perhaps also in the cytoplasm. It is suggested that when the male-determining substance in such organisms is consistently emitted in excess of the female-determining, the organism is normally a male, but that if there are irregularities in the rate at which the two substances, male-determining and female-determining, are produced, you will get the influence shown first of one and then of the other. The theory can be made to fit the anomalies of intersex and of sex-reversal to which I have referred, and geneticists who believe that the chromosomes actually determine characters such as sex apparently do not consider that to assume the existence and the modifying interactions of these hypothetical substances—which may come from the cytoplasm itself—in any way weakens their statement that in the chromosomes reside the actual deter-

minants. It is not for me here to embark on further discussion of the evidence adduced. In this chapter I am
concerned merely with the general tendencies in biology in
1929; so here I do no more than point out that, in considering the theoretical aspects of their work, modern
geneticists are more disposed than they were ten years ago
to recognize the extreme complexity of the problems that
engage them and to give increased attention to the interaction and the balance of factors, wherever these reside,
which go to the production of the results expressed in the
organism.

The hypothetical substances emitted by the genes in the
chromosomes or by the cytoplasm itself are not to be
confused with certain secretions of the body cells, collectively grouped as 'secretions of the endocrine organs'.
Some of these can be isolated and their composition is in
part known; the action of others has been demonstrated
satisfactorily enough by experiment. One of the most important additions to our knowledge of the working of the
body of a living animal has resulted from study of these
'internal secretions'. We know now that certain tissues
normally secrete substances that are passed directly into
the blood-stream and, there circulating, produce effects in
tissues often far removed from the seat of elaboration.
Such tissues form the bulk of 'ductless glands' like the
thyroid, the adrenals, and the pituitary body. Sometimes
the secreting cells are not collected into a definitely
localized gland. The entry into the intestine of food from
the stomach stimulates the cells lining the intestine to
produce a substance, secretin, which, cast into the blood,
goes round the body until it reaches the pancreas, when it
in turn stimulates that organ to produce its characteristic
digestive juice. The secretions of the thyroid and pituitary
regulate the growth and harmonious development of the
body: the secretions of certain cells in the reproductive

glands determine the development of the secondary sexual characters—such as the horns of deer and the male plumage of many birds. Work on endocrines is still only in the experimental stage, but already practical results of immense value to medicine are available. I need only mention the benefit that properly administered thyroid extract brings to the growing child whose own thyroid is for some reason secreting less than the normal, and the relief brought to many sufferers from diabetes by the injection into their blood of insulin which the endocrine tissues in their own pancreatic glands are failing to produce in sufficient quantity to regulate the body's carbohydrate metabolism.

One outcome of the most recent experimental work in endocrinology is recognition of the interdependence of the various secreting tissues on one another. Let me give you an example. When the egg of a mammal breaks away from the ovary, there develops from the degenerating tissue in the place where it lay a body known as the corpus luteum. This proves to be an important endocrine organ, which probably manufactures two distinct secretions with different functions; and these secretions from the corpora lutea control the ability of the uterus to detain in it the descending fertilized egg, control also the length of the gestation period in the pregnant female and the oncome of the secreting activity of the milk-glands when the young is born. But we find also that another substance, coming from the pituitary body below the brain and far from the seat of action in the reproductive organs, has the function of setting the whole process a-going, and possibly also determines the length of time that the various part-processes shall take. It seems that ovulation in the mammal follows in response to stimulation by a secretion from the anterior lobe of the pituitary, and that the subsequent formation of the endocrinal corpora lutea, where the ova drop out, is also under the control of this chemical messenger from a distant source.

In the nineteenth century the study of embryology was regarded as interesting mainly for the evidence it afforded of the fundamental relationships of animals. The similarity of the developing reptile, bird, and mammal was witness to the real affinities of these very different vertebrates, scaled, feathered, and hairy. And to further the acceptance of the doctrine of organic evolution comparative embryology was exhaustively exploited for many years. But interest in embryology has shifted to a new standpoint, and we are investigating the phenomena of ontogeny with a new and more subtle technique. Having studied normal development, the embryologist now subjects the developing creature to unnatural environments; he places it in media polluted by introduced chemicals, he turns the X-rays upon it, he removes living structures from the body and transplants them into new positions, or he grafts portions of one embryo on to the body of another. And as he explores the plasticity of the organism by these experimental methods, the biologist becomes increasingly aware of the interactions of the various parts within the whole; he realizes more clearly than he did that the degree of development of one structure affects the subsequent development of others; and he comes more and more to feel that the whole is more than the sum of its parts.

We learn now that the seeming contradictions in the discoveries made by the earlier experimenters, where these were honestly recorded and interpreted, are not really so contradictory as first appeared. We learn that both schools were right—the men who declared that if you separated the first cells of a developing embryo, they would each grow into a small, but reasonably complete creature, and the men who declared that this did not happen, but that the egg was already so well organized, and the embryo already so 'pre-formed' within it, that a part could not possibly give rise to the whole. We know now that for certain organisms the first statement holds true, and for

certain others the second. We have learnt that, somewhere
in the course of development, there comes a stage beyond
which 'regulation' becomes increasingly difficult, if not
impossible; but that this stage comes on earlier in some
animals than in others. If you separate completely the
first two cells of the frog's egg, each can be induced to
grow into a complete half-sized animal; but if you similarly
separate the early blastomeres of a ctenophore, the result
will be a monster. Some organisms are more plastic in the
early stages, and some are more 'set'. In the sea-urchin, for
instance, the subject of Driesch's classic experiments regarding the regulating power of the organism, the modern
experimenter finds that the embryo remains an 'harmonic
equipotential system' right up to the blastula stage and
even during early gastrulation. But if you cut up the
corresponding stage of a newt's embryo you find that, if
the neural folds have begun to form, the organism has lost
its power to readjust the proportions of the developing
parts, and the resulting embryo from the animal pole of the
reduced material will have a spinal cord out of all proportion to the rest of its body. The idea of an 'organizer' has
been introduced; in some embryos the organizer appears
early; in others it appears relatively late. The modern
view of the organizing process, based on what has been
learnt from the experimental method, 'makes it possible
to sort out the developmental processes logically and to
appreciate better their causal connexion one with the
other'.

The experimentalist has grafted limbs and eyes from
one embryo into the body of another, and he has seen how
the introduction of these implants influences the out-
growth of muscles and nerves in the body of the 'host'. He
destroys, for instance, the nerve cord of a developing newt;
then he removes its limbs so that they lose all connexion
with the nerves that should supply them and induce them
to move; and then he plants them in their normal position

in the body of another newt with a perfectly good spinal cord. He finds that they become normally innervated from the host's spinal cord; and this takes place so long as he does not make the implant too far from the natural position of limbs on the trunk. If he departs too far from this—if, for instance he plants a limb on the head—he finds that one of the cranial nerves, ordinarily supplying the throat, will take over the job of supplying the muscles of the ingrafted leg! How do the nerves of the host animal find their sure way to the implanted limb? What is the interaction between the muscle and the nerve that sets growth a-going in the right direction? Or is there any such interaction? It has been shown that in normally developing amphibians the nerves supplying the muscles of the trunk send new branches into the young limb before the limb is able to move, and the nerves of the tongue grow into that organ before there is any muscular tissue for them to supply.

In elucidating problems such as these the recent development of the technique of tissue-culture may yet play an important part. For the biologist has also learnt how to remove living tissues from an animal and keep them alive and growing in sterile glass vessels where he feeds them on serum and other suitable substances. Tissue from the heart of an embryo chick has been kept alive and growing for over ten years—longer, that is to say, than is the normal span of life of the bird to which the heart once belonged. Tissues differ very much in their power to preserve their especial characters in culture. Kidney and cartilage usually go back into a primitive undifferentiated condition; epithelium and connective tissue dedifferentiate almost at once. The muscle of the heart of a chick, on the other hand, remains *as muscle*, and in culture its cells continue to contract actively as muscle should. Nerve-cells grow well in culture and throw out thread-like branches which, within the body, would form the axes of nerve-fibres: and experiment shows that the direction of these fibres can be influenced by the electric current. I mention this because it has been suggested that nerve-cells in the spinal cord of the newt into which a limb was implanted act like conductors, and that an electric current is generated in the living body that causes them to throw out new branches at right angles to the cord, and so in the direction of the limb that they are to supply.

But one of the most interesting revelations of tissue culture is the dependence of one tissue on another for its power to differentiate. I said just now that if you grow epithelium and connective tissue *separately* in pure culture, both quickly lose the characters especially distinctive of them. But grow them together, and they retain the morphological features that distinguish them within the body. Pure kidney tissue quickly reverts to an embryonic state; but add some connective tissue to the culture, and it re-differentiates and produces characteristic kidney tubules. Or grow cartilage for a long time *in vitro* and sub-culture until you are quite certain that there is none of the original material left; then you may graft some of this undifferentiated stuff back into the body of a suitable animal, and, in contact there with other tissues, it will turn again into typical gristle.

And we find that we can extract from embryos a substance which, added to a tissue-culture, stimulates that to increased growth. The tissues of an adult animal do not normally yield any such stimulating extract. But if you injure certain adult tissues and then incubate them at body-temperature, they will produce a powerful growth stimulant which exerts its influence on a tissue-culture for about two days. Now perhaps something of this kind happens in the animal body when tissues are damaged and have to be repaired by the addition of fresh cells at the place of mending.

Tissue-culture may help us solve some of the problems

connected with abnormal growth, as of tumours. When a tumour appears something has happened that induces the adult body-cells to start off dividing in a way they would not ordinarily do at that age. The juices extracted from tumours behave like the extracts from injured tissues to which I have just referred. Only, unfortunately, their potency is not exhausted at the end of two days; and the more malignant the tumour, the more stimulating are the substances it yields and the longer does the stimulating effect endure.

Now let me take another aspect. By the term 'symbiosis' the biologist refers to the curious phenomenon of association between two organisms of different kinds for the benefit of both. The association may be rather loose and external, as in the case of the hermit-crab and its camouflage of sea-anemones; or it may be extraordinarily intimate, as when one organism lives within the body, or actually within the tissues, of its partner. In the latter type of association the mutual adaptation and dependence may have gone so far that the two concerned cannot flourish when separated. The name 'symbiosis' is usually restricted to the more intimate partnerships, while the others are spoken of as 'commensalism'; but the difference between the two kinds is only one of degree. It should be noted, moreover, that the line between symbiosis and what we call parasitism is not very sharply drawn (in a case of true parasitism one partner is drawing all the benefit and may indeed prove very injurious to its host), and indeed there is some indication that many mutually beneficial partnerships have evolved from an initial experimental stage of parasitism by one of the members, in which the exploited species has successfully reacted in such a way as to acquire, not merely immunity from injury, but actually so much material benefit that it has come to terms with its old enemy and agreed to take him into the business. Certain cases of symbiosis have long been known, and every text-book on biology holds some reference to them; but I think it is characteristic of the modern outlook that the extent and the importance of these interdependences should be increasingly recognized and understood.

We have again explored the complicated society of the ant and of the termite, and though still much puzzled by many of the facts observed, we are nearer than we were ten years ago to appreciating the mutually beneficial relations existing between the insects and the plants that dwell together there. The green-fly are housed and taken out to pasture by the ants in return for the honey-dew they yield; the strange symphilic beetles dwelling in the ant-heap also secrete, many of them, pleasant juices prized by their protectors; the carefully sheltered fungus-gardens provide both ants and termites with nourishment and also with substances which, when swallowed, enable the insects to digest cellulose. And those termites that do not culti-vate fungus, but live solely on fresh wood—and they are the great majority—actually carry round with them in their intestines hordes of microscopic animals, found no-where else in nature, and so specialized in structure and in habit that they cannot live apart from their termite partners. It used to be supposed that these organisms were some sort of parasites against which the infected white ants had acquired immunity though they could not throw them off. But now we know that a symbiotic association of a peculiar and most intimate kind exists between the two. Recent experiments have proved beyond all shadow of a doubt that the mysterious inhabitants of the termite's gut have, like a fungus, the power of splitting up the cellulose of which wood is largely composed, and thus of preparing for their host's assimilation the essential material which these insects, like the vast majority of animals, are unable to digest for themselves. Many similar cases of sym-biosis are now suspected among other wood-eating insects and the bacteria and yeasts that shelter in special pockets of their digestive tracts. And the mysterious 'phosphorescence' of certain marine animals, of value to them probably in scaring off their enemies or in attracting their mates at the breeding season, has been shown in some instances to be the contribution offered by bacteria which live sheltered and protected lives within the bodies of their partners, and are apparently of such value to the species that they are handed on in suitable quantities to the young when the eggs are laid.

In the latter half of the nineteenth century the study of the geographical distribution of plants and animals received great impetus from the work of Darwin and of Wallace, who, as young naturalists, accumulated a vast amount of evidence to show that the present-day distribution is explicable only on the assumption that there has been slow organic evolution. The foundations laid in the nineteenth century have stood firm: the broad principles of animal and plant distribution are accepted, and intensive exploration has added so much to our knowledge, that mere collecting, for collecting's sake, has ceased to interest any but the confirmed systematist. Biologists are now concerning themselves rather with the more subtle problems that, so to speak, precede, and are implicit in, the problems of radiation and dispersal. The geographer is becoming an ecologist.

It was interesting to learn there are no deer in Africa south of the Sahara and no monkeys in Madagascar, though perfectly good forests abound in both places where, one would suppose, deer or monkeys might well live in comfort. And the explanation of these absences offered by the zoogeographers of last century was stimulating to the imagination and taught us much concerning the secular wanderings of animals and the possibilities of the evolution of new forms with change of habitat. But it does not satisfy the modern biologist to know that there are no deer in Africa south of the Sahara because, at a time when the first deer were moving southward from their Holarctic home, a great sea or a desert stretching across north Africa set bounds to their migration. The modern biologist wants to know more, for instance, about the life of deer as *deer*, or about the life of monkeys as *monkeys*; what they feed on, what is their rate of reproduction, what are their enemies, their diseases? What happens to them when you introduce them into a new country? And so of rats, of badgers, of sparrows, of salmon, of beetles. What are the secrets of their lives? What makes them happy? What do they fear? Why do they flourish here and not there? What factors, climatic and biotic, control their destinies?

And directly we begin to investigate such matters, we find ourselves in the unknown, but, as we believe, not in the unknowable. To elucidate even the least of these questions will take a life-time of patient observation in the field and study in the laboratory, for at the very outset we are met with complicating side-issues of all kinds, any one of which is well worth following out for the light it may throw upon the whole question of inter-relation and of ultimate dependences. We have all been taught to believe in 'the web of life'. We know, or at least we are taught, that no animal or plant lives to or for itself, and vaguely we feel this to be true. But to agree to such a statement is a very different matter from proving that it is true in any concrete instance. We believe that Darwin was not merely being epigrammatic when he said that the number of cats depended on the clover-crop. But few of us would know enough about the biotic environment of any animal to work out the 'food-chain' between clover and cats as, with his innate genius for ecology, he very neatly and convincingly could. At least, however, we have become alive to our ignorance, and are attempting to remedy the defect; the next fifty years is going to bring to light more clearly some part of the *pattern* in that web of life to the existence of which we subscribe, though we violate the guidance of its woof and warp every day of our lives.

In the study of scientific ecology the botanist made a beginning earlier than did the zoologist, and he has gone much further. There are fewer species of plants than of animals, and plant-life, on the whole, is much more stereotyped than is the life of animals. Moreover, a plant will stay still in the same place long enough for you to get a chance to see what is happening to it and what it is trying to do. The problem facing the animal ecologist is more difficult and more complex. Animals are, for the most part, so restless, and in their behaviour and their needs so various; a fox and a rabbit, for instance, differ from one another so much more than do a whin-bush and a cabbage. But already, from the facts collected and correlated by a few men with the right imaginative quality and the right practical equipment—'a slight, but not superficial, knowledge of many sciences'—there is growing up a new understanding of animal life in Nature, an under-standing that, if I mistake not, will ultimately guide intelligently not only our attempts at naturalization of animals in new countries and our control of 'pests', but also perhaps, to some extent, our conscious control of the social life of the animal, man himself.

We are developing the idea of the 'animal association'. We see that each natural habitat contains a characteristic set of animals, which are not there by chance, so to speak, but must maintain themselves successfully, each in its rightful niche, if the whole association is not to fall to pieces. We see that these associations can be studied from the point of view of their dependence on one another for food-supply, and we proceed to work out the 'food-chains' linking one kind of animal with another: all the food-chains within an association constitute its 'food-cycle'. In a pine-wood, small green-fly feed on the juices of the leaves; the insects are preyed on by certain spiders; tits and warblers eat the spiders and are in turn the prey of hawks. In the sea, as on the land, plants form the basic food-supply; these are not, for the most part, large, conspicuous plants, such as the sea-weeds of our shallower waters—but minute algae and diatoms floating near the surface, individually invisible to the naked eye, but so numerous at times that the whole sea is turned a different colour by their presence. And on these plants live countless myriads of floating animals—the active young of most sedentary sea-beasts and the young and adult forms of many others—and among these latter are the small crustacea that we call the cope-pods and the euphausids. And on these little crustacea prey the fishes and even the great whale-bone whales; and on the smaller fishes depend for food the larger fishes, and on these again some of the toothed whales and the seals, and ultimately the polar bears. So you will understand that the abundance of the organism at what we may call the inner end of the food-chain will affect the abundance of the whole series of creatures dependent on it, whether directly or indirectly, and so the balance of the association generally. There are 'key-industries' in Nature as well as in the civilizations of man. And knowledge of what affects their success or failure from season to season has its practical bearing on many economic problems. For at the end of certain food-chains stands man himself, and it may be very much to his interest to know whether certain important food-fishes, such as the herring, will be abundant on the fishing-grounds when he goes out for the annual catch. There are whole towns on the Baltic Sea that depend for their very life on the success of the herring season. Like animal and plant breeding, the herring fishery has always been a great gamble, but the biologist is working in an international scheme with the meteorologist and the hydrographer to lessen the uncertainty; and one of the most important contributions he is making to the problem is a more exact knowledge of the herring's feeding habits and of the conditions determining its ultimate food-supply at all stages in its life.

And from study of the balance of food-chains in the food-cycle emerges the fact that the enemy of the individual is often the friend of the species. Red deer were introduced into New Zealand in the fifties of last century, and after many preliminary failures were established in those islands to which no mammal is indigenous. They found themselves in a country suitable in climate and rich in pleasant saplings, from which they proceeded to strip the bark and the young leaves. They waxed fat and larger than the normal deer of their northern homes; the males went on begetting young long after the period of their best maturity. No fierce carnivores, no wolves or eagles, lived in these happy islands, so the red deer and their young were safe from attack. But presently their reproductiveness began to alarm the colonists who had introduced them; the animals were over-running the country and exterminating many valuable plants. They never became such a curse as did the rabbit and the bramble and the lark, introduced by the settlers in much the same haphazard way; but their depredations were serious enough. Then almost before the anxious farmers could take up wholesale measures for reduction of the deer, Nature herself stepped in and the plague began mysteriously to diminish. The food-supply for such great herds began to run short, too much inbreeding and too frequent mating with old males began to weaken the stock; the animals became smaller, their horns showed abnormalities, they fell a prey to disease which, in healthier conditions, they could have withstood. And gradually, by this process of weeding out and the diminished fertility resultant on food-shortage, a balance was struck between the new colonists and their environment; their numbers were reduced until the danger of a deer pest disappeared and they became reasonably unexacting members of

the new community in which they had established themselves.

And this story has its dramatic parallel in all that we
know of rabbit plagues and mouse plagues and the spread
of noxious weeds. We see that natural checks—'enemies'
as we call them—tend to keep a species within the limits
where it can multiply with safety to itself and where its
young will find sufficient food to satisfy their needs. If the
checks are removed, as happens when man ignorantly
introduces, for sentimental or utilitarian reasons, his
favourite animals or plants into countries where their
natural enemies are lacking, or where, as sometimes
happens in the native country, the carnivores at the outer
end of the food-chain fail to do their part, there is always
a corresponding outburst of reproduction in the sub-
sidiary links, sometimes amounting to a plague; then
follows starvation and disease, or the animals native to
the new country develop a taste for the flesh of the new-
comers and so take over the work of pruning, and there
follows a return to more normal conditions.

Before the War this ignorant introduction of animals
and plants went on almost unchecked. Now it is becoming
less and less possible. For governments have learnt something of the biologist's lesson, and every civilized country
is busily protecting itself against such undesirable immigrants; plague prevention is relatively simple, but the
effective cure is hard. Where the pest is already established, the biologist, given a free hand, is learning how to
introduce effective biological control to cope with plagues
that have defied extermination by chemical means. In
this way the apple industry in New Zealand, threatened
with complete ruin by the unintentional introduction of the
woolly aphis blight, has in the last few years been saved by
skilful introduction of one of its enemies, an American
wasp; and the prickly pear in Australia, which in comparatively few years put 30 million acres of country out of

I

cultivation, has been got in hand by the timely introduction of two little scale insects which are among its natural enemies in its native home. But it is a ticklish business, this bringing in of animal controls! Living organisms are alarmingly adaptable, and the introduced enemy may easily develop a taste for a new diet and turn his attention to some plant of economic importance. Or it may develop enemies of its own in the new country, so powerful and so effective that its establishment in numbers sufficient to deal with the farmer's pest becomes impossible.

We are only at the beginning of such work; but undoubtedly every year that adds to our knowledge of the habits and tastes of animals and enables us to analyse their food-chains further, gives us, by the way, something that we may turn to very practical account.

And much of what we learn concerning living organisms should be applicable to man himself, who, from the biologist's point of view, is one with the animals. A better understanding of what underlies the seeming inconsequences of hereditary transmission is necessary if we may hope to breed a finer race of men; and increased knowledge of the interrelations between the animals and plants around us may give us some hint from time to time towards solution of the problems within the peculiar animal society that is human.

BOOKS FOR REFERENCE

G. R. de Beer. *An Introduction to Experimental Embryology.* Oxford University Press, 1926.

—— *Embryology and Evolution.* Oxford University Press, 1930.

F. W. R. Brambell. *Development of Sex in Vertebrates.* Sidgwick & Jackson, 1930.

P. A. Buxton. *Animal Life in Deserts.* Arnold & Co., 1923.

C. Elton. *Animal Ecology.* Sidgwick & Jackson, 1927.

—— *Ecology and Evolution.* Oxford University Press, 1930.

J. B. S. Haldane and J. S. Huxley. *Animal Biology.* Oxford University Press, 1927.

H. G. Wells, J. S. Huxley, and G. P. Wells. *The Science of Life.* Cassells, 1931.

VII

CONTEMPORARY EDUCATION

By F. S. MARVIN

How far can we use the world's schools and colleges as a mirror of a new world order? Only to a limited extent, for it is not the function of schools to lead the way in social change, but to prepare each new generation to take its place in an existing order. They reflect, of course, new things which are establishing themselves in the public mind, but they cannot initiate them, for they are dealing with minds to which the whole world is new, and one must understand things existing before beginning with any hope of success to reform them. Education therefore, especially in its earlier stages, must necessarily have a conservative bearing, for it would be disastrous if every new denizen of the world entered it feeling that there was nothing fixed on which he could rely, that all his surroundings were in a state of flux, and that it was rather more likely that he would sink than swim. Something to be sure of and proud of, this should be the starting-point; then later may come the hopeful desire to make the world better by one's own endeavour. All education systems of the past have had this character at their best, and it is the right spirit in a well-established civilization with traditions of renown.

Surveying the world of schools since the War, we notice, as might be expected, that there has been least change in those countries which have escaped political revolution. Everywhere there has been a marked access of interest in education, but it has taken on an ardent and propagandist form in the new states anxious to fortify their nations. So it is in Poland, Rumania, or Czechoslovakia, so also in Soviet Russia, where a new economic gospel has to be spread through schools and colleges. In an old country like Germany, with rich traditions, which has suffered a severe political revolution, the schools have been torn by rival influences. In the effort, therefore, to keep the balance true between the old and new in their own history, they have not yet settled down to realize the new order which has been growing up meanwhile in the world around them.

Hence for various reasons in different countries the new internationalism is not prominent in places of teaching; it bulks more largely in the realm of learning. But in spite of this there can be no doubt of the whole-hearted adherence of the teaching body throughout the world to the cause of peace; methods of permeating the curriculum and influencing the scholars remain to be discussed; but the goal to be aimed at is already fixed in the minds of ninety per cent. of those who have the work to do.

But before turning to the content of the systematic education found in schools and examinations, one general caution is needed. It would be as great an error to identify this system with education as a whole as to treat the League of Nations as summing up the world co-operation of which this book treats. In each case the official organ is the symbol and chief agent of the process, but by no means covers it. The education of every one is far larger than what he receives in school and consists of the mass of influences which bear upon him from birth to maturity. The fuller the life of any community the greater the part played in education by these outside forces. In a remote and primitive village community, such as that described in Mr. McKee's recent fascinating book,[1] a vigorous school may become the most formative influence in the lives of the young inhabitants. In a full and progressive society such as ours there are a hundred other things at work to form the growing mind beside the lessons and other activities prescribed by the school. The family, the cinema, the wireless, the library, the street, the boy

[1] *New Schools for Young India*. Oxford University Press.

scouts, are a few of the more obvious. The schoolmaster among us may be a proud man, for he is rare, who, meeting a scholar in after years, hears him say, 'You gave me my bent for life'.

Of all the features of education since the War, perhaps the most striking is the greater activity of all governments in that sphere. Everywhere they are spending more, and everywhere in cónnexion with the spending goes a greater amount of suggestion, direction, and organization. This concern for organization is a marked feature in the school policy since the War of England and Sweden, and involves a larger intervention of the State. Organization in these cases consists mainly in fitting together different classes of schools, those of private and those of public origin, and seeing that scholars in their transfer gain the fullest advantage for their age. A special feature in the Swedish system in recent years is the establishment of a widespread network of Folks Higher Schools on the Danish model to which we in England have no close parallel. The fact that they are able in these countries to obtain the continuous attendance of adults in boarding establishments for several months is a striking proof of their zeal for education, but is also due largely to the agricultural pursuits of their people.

England has been studying Swedish reforms of the period, but has not yet been able to take any marked step forward. There have been many obstacles. The first was that, during the War, a Bill was hastily passed raising the school age generally to sixteen, and providing for certain continuation classes up to eighteen. The country as a whole was not ripe for it, nor the teaching staff adequate, and the expenses of post-War years have left it still in abeyance. Attempts are being made to arrange a grouping of the primary schools by which the older scholars might be placed in central schools and obtain more adequate and advanced instruction. In 1930 a Bill which would have raised the age to fifteen and made easier this re-grouping, passed the House of Commons, but was finally rejected in the Lords, partly on the grounds of expense, partly for religious reasons, partly because of a certain scepticism as to the superiority in every case of school education over work in the fields or elsewhere, especially for the older boys.

Are we to say, then, that education—even popular education—in England has stood still since the War? Nothing would be further from the truth. There has never been a time of greater activity both in the schools and without. In reviewing the signs of this one must give first place to the rising spirit of the teaching body. Teachers, especially those in the popular schools, continue to be the profession most anxious to improve its efficiency in after years by attendance at lectures, by visits to other schools, by foreign travel. They form the bulk of the conferences which are now so familiar a feature of the summer months both in Europe and America. And it is to them that we may look with more confidence than to any other profession for the united and passionate support of world-peace and world-co-operation. There was in Stockholm in August 1931 a European convention of teachers from France and Germany as well as the Scandinavian countries, and the depth of feeling evinced by these people, in closest touch with the minds of the rising generation, might convince those sceptical about Geneva that some new thing had come into the world.

The teaching body, indeed, is thus in earnest throughout the world, and if the results of their labour seem sometimes disappointing, it is not to be attributed to any want of zeal, but to the uncalculated difficulty of their task and the short time in which they have been trying to do it. It is very welcome, therefore, to find any clear and scientific evidence as to the effects of the new educational effort. The best document is the *New Survey of London Life and Labour*, which takes up after forty years the work of

Charles Booth and proposes to give a picture of the advance made in that period. At present only the summary introductory volume has appeared, but its most striking passages bear on education and its results. Both in health, crime, and recreation the various authors of this report seem confident that they can trace the effects of the compulsory system of elementary education which has been at work ih London for the forty or fifty years of which they speak; and London is typical at least of the great urban areas in Great Britain.

All the main sides on which a comparison can be drawn between London now and London then show to the advantage of the present, and the improvement is most marked in physical health. The progress of public health, say the reporters, has benefited immensely both from the direct and indirect effects of the London education service. A reading and discriminating public has been substituted for an illiterate and ignorant public, and a public opinion has grown up which now supports instead of thwarting the sanitary reformer. The saving of child-life is the most striking statistical result, for the rate of infant mortality fell in a way unexpected by the most sanguine doctors, as soon as a generation had passed through the primary schools and become the parents of a new generation. In the records of crime the tendency is also in the right direction and also to be connected with education. But it is not so marked or so unqualified. Larceny and crimes of violence have diminished, but latterly there has been a certain increase in cases of false pretence and frauds involving ingenuity, and some—but not an alarming—increase in sexual offences. On the side of recreation they claim a superiority for the cinema over the public-house, and point to the large extension of public libraries in the period and the growing use in them of the more serious books.

It is a fair judgement, and one must rejoice in the unmistakable improvement in health and the joyous use of the playgrounds which public and private energy are opening all over the country. The days of poor Jo and Tom-all-alone seem now as remote from us as the Middle Ages and far more horrible. And this is the impression conveyed by English schools and child-life on the intelligent foreigner, who often sees us better than we can see ourselves. The happiest country for the young, is now a very general verdict. Dickens and the humanitarians of the last century raised the standard for this advance, in which England is only at one with all civilized industrial countries, but in which she has been able by the greater unity of her social effort to attain a leading place.

Health, happiness, and a freedom in individual initiative are now the marks of any treatment of the young which commands general admiration, and it is a sound instinct, for these are the necessary prerequisites in childhood to sound development in after years. But it will be noted that in taking up this attitude we have not advanced beyond the revolutionary stage, the cult of nature. Rousseau might have said all that we now say under these headings. When we come to the training of the mind there is much less unanimity. Systems differ as to the amount of knowledge which should be imparted to the young, and as to the stress to be laid on special subjects and vocational bias. On the Continent generally far more is learnt than in England or the United States, and while with us the ideal most followed is the training of character, with knowledge and vocation as subordinate, in America the tendency is to allow more latitude of choice as to subjects while giving practical or vocational work a freer entry into general education. Nowhere yet, except in some occasional, specially devised institution, is an effort made throughout the school to train the pupils as future members of a world-community, knowing enough of its languages and putting in the first place a sense of the reality of international relations.

That this must come is certain, and it would be pleasant to trace the efforts that are being made here and there to reach it. But it will be more useful and truer to the facts to indicate briefly the mass of work that still holds the field and hinders the most internationally minded teachers from pursuing a wider course.

The dominant facts are obvious. The growth of knowledge beyond all precedent, the world more interlocked and complicated every year by the applications of this knowledge, the life into which the young are to be plunged, more exacting in its requirements; and to meet this no proportionate expansion of the young brain, no lengthening of the day, no adequate improvement of the technique of teaching. The English ideal, excellent as it is, actually adds another, and perhaps the most formidable, obstacle in the way of acquiring knowledge and training the mind. For knowledge in the English system is a secondary matter, and 'character' should be supreme, and character is better formed by other methods than by poring over books or exercising the mind on abstract problems which, if valuable at all, are only fit for later years. Thus the outline of the history of philosophy, which finds a place in the classes of higher French and German schools, would be scouted in England. The playing fields and the boy scouts or the O.T.C. are the schools of character, and in supporting them practically all classes in England are in agreement, to the great advantage of the nation. In times of strike our strikers and police play football together, while in unhappy Germany Nazi and Communist lie in wait for one another at the street corners with mortal weapons.

But there is another side to the question. The world, we hope, is ceasing to be a blood-stained battle-field, but is not destined to be a universal playground. The man trained to find his chief expression and delight in pure play finds reality a troublesome thing, when at last he is brought up against it. Sometimes, as an individual, he goes down

in the struggle, or, as a nation, he and his compeers are
reduced to the humiliating practice of 'muddling through'.
But such commonplaces, though they may command a
formal assent, do not take us far in the task of reforming
practice. A few glimpses at the actual will be more to
the point.

Language, mathematics, science, history, these are the
staple of a school education, and every one who stays till
fifteen or sixteen learns something of all of them. Each
of them obstructs as well as assists the attainment of an
education more adequate to the new conditions of the
world. All are necessary and the teaching would be
improved by a process of concurrent simplification and
synthesis. The teaching of language bulks largest in early
education, and on this therefore a few remarks may first be
made.

An able and enterprising Spaniard has lately started a
school near Madrid where all the children are to be taught
the five languages of the Western Republic—French,
English, German, and Italian, as well as their native
Spanish. Auguste Comte had the same idea and, like his
idea of a thirteen-month calendar, it has hitherto remained
in the realm of utopias until Señor Castillejo took it up the
other day and says that he means to persist; it will be
interesting to see with what results. One may be sure,
however, that he will not persuade the majority of schools
which are at the same time besieged by the claims of some
new universal language. Esperanto leads the van, but it is
challenged by many others, and the advocates of a
simplified form of English seem gaining ground. We
need to think out carefully the many various aims
involved.

Primarily, there is the supreme international aim of
securing some medium by which human intercourse may
be rendered easier. There is also the intellectual value of
translating one's thoughts from their native medium into

the currency of another people, similar to ourselves but
with the innumerable nuances due to difference in history
and social habits.[1] The preservation of these differences is
also an object of no small value from the point of view of
history and of blending national diversity with essential
unity. The last object becomes in the case of the many
small nations of to-day the most formidable practical difficulty in language training and the spread of human community through language. In the solution of the problem
no doubt the necessities of trade and travel will play the
leading part. Freedom of choice and the encouragement
of the easiest means of intercourse will in most areas
favour the spread of English. A living and growing
language has always resources within itself, while it is at
once the natural medium with the millions of those who
speak it and with the thousands of those who have com-
mitted permanent thoughts to it in the past. But, if English
is thus to spread, it must be introduced in a simpler
rational form;[2] while, as a general canon of education,
for English people as well as others, it should be accepted
that a knowledge of at least one other language than his
own is necessary for every one. Is this too much to ask
when Señor Castillejo is teaching four foreign modern
languages to his little Spaniards?

As things now are, although so little linguistic facility is
as a rule acquired, far too large a proportion of school time
is consumed in acquiring it. This is true of schools
generally, but especially of those countries where a
language, spoken by few and of small contemporary
value, is being forced on the scholars for political reasons.
Freedom to speak it for those who wish, and the most
scrupulous care of its literary remains for historical

[1] See 'Language as a Link' in *Western Races and the World*
(Unity Series V).
[2] See *Basic English*, by C. K. Ogden (Kegan Paul), and *Anglia*,
by Professor Zachrisson of Upsala.

reasons, these seem the reasonable lines for meeting the case. But, for the scholar and the future, the supreme consideration must be how to make the best use of his time in school for his general good, and how to make him the most efficient member of a new world-order embracing all mankind.

Similar thoughts are applicable to the teaching of the great languages of the past, which appeal to large populations both East and West. Latin and Greek represent in literature the foundation of Western civilization. Sanskrit stands in much the same position for the Hindu, classical Arabic for the Moslem, and Hebrew for the Jew. In each case it is rather the historical than the linguistic reason which keeps the study alive. Their value is inestimable, and if civilization is to retain its historical continuity, educated men will continue to turn to them. But the original purpose of a medium of communication has passed away, and the derivative purpose of mental training is now largely taken by other studies. Hence the most fervent admirer of classical literature, the strongest believer in the value of the historical spirit, may hold that too much time on the average is given to Latin, or, in Egyptian schools, to Arabic, and that with a change of spirit or technique the desired result could be more easily obtained. The more such studies are linked up with history the better for culture; the more the linguistic forces of education are turned on to the best in modern languages, the better for the unity of civilization.

The modern knowledge which knocks most imperatively at the doors of the schools is, of course, science and technology. As these studies prepare for an increasing part of the work by which the scholars will have to live, it is not surprising that their claim is being heard all over the world, and that a larger share of teaching power and financial support is given every year to laboratories and educational workshops. It is both necessary and right, and the justification is seen most clearly in countries such as India, Egypt, China, or Japan, where difficulties of language, religion, or historical tradition make an effective education in 'humane letters' so difficult. The student who loses himself in the nuances of literature, if he ever wins through far enough to contemplate them at all, may find an easier outlet and reasonable satisfaction in physical science. Here there is a common language and a possibility for self-expression unhampered by the idioms of grammar or the moral differences of class or race. The laboratory, being popular, turns out better work and affords welcome evidence both of the universal appeal of science and the general high level of human intelligence. Given equal opportunity, the Easterner, or any student coming fresh to Western science or technology, is at no such disadvantage as meets him in politics, philosophy, or literature. He will hold his own, and may seriously compete, perhaps on a more superficial plane, with the more deeply grounded Westerner. The moral for the Westerner, and of Westerners most of all for the Englishman, is, while standing firm on his national and European foundation, to quicken his methods and widen his outlook.

Synthesis and simplification would both find ample scope here, and a discourse on the combined teaching of science and mathematics would take us far afield. Only one or two points are possible, strictly relevant to our theme of contemporary education and a new world-order.

Mathematics stand to physical science much in that relation of a universal language which is being demanded for business and politics. This side, therefore, of the subject would naturally be made prominent in any teaching which had in view the strengthening of the links which bind all thinking men together. Unfortunately, in England, so far is this from being done that only in a small minority of cases is the ordinary scholar ever introduced to the calculus which is the one vital link between modern mathematics and science. Owing partly to tradition, partly to the extravagances of examination, the calculus which is the most fascinating aspect of mathematics and within the scope of the average child of fifteen, is relegated either to the most advanced stage or the special work of the engineer.

It is interesting to notice that in this matter, as in a good many others, outside agencies are ready to do in their haphazard way what the school has left undone. Scores of popular books on all branches of modern knowledge are constantly appearing which introduce the rising generation to the calculus or sex or aviation, and leave the reader free to make what use he pleases of the information. There was never a time when the public was so well catered for in this respect, and the abundance marks the gap which exists between the formal and the real education which is going on. It is largely inevitable in an age when men's views of the nature of things are growing and changing from day to day, and when the searchlight of science spreads over so wide a field. No one could wish the latest theory of the atom to be expounded in the daily lessons of the classroom only to be replaced by another to-morrow. But certain cardinal points stand out permanently. These should be made clear and brought home to every one, especially if they are of the kind on which the whole structure of thought and of society are coming to rest. The calculus has for long belonged to this class. Relativity and the League of Nations belong to it to-day.

There is a striking and very important feature common to these three great achievements of human thought and action and to many others which might be named. They are all triumphs of the synthetic spirit, and the question then arises in a general form how far in contemporary education an effort is being made to impress this aspect of thought upon the scholars and in what ways it might be further done. As to the need there can be no question.

Man is faced by an external universe and a society of extreme and growing complexity. His only salvation lies in finding and making order in the diversity; on that road he has reached the state of imperfect peace in which he now stands, and the need of a further advance is at the moment more urgent than ever. Surely the age of adolescence, when the mind is most malleable and the rising generation still more or less under the control of the adult, should be used for enforcing that direction of life which we are agreed is essential for the general good? Propaganda, if you will; but, as all deliberate education is propaganda in one direction or another, the only practical question is whether you wish the education to tend to a state of mental harmony and strength or to leave the educand at the end of it rudderless in a sea of cross currents and conflicting ideas and emotions. We train for service, is the current and excellent motto of the day, but service of what and how? We cannot answer these questions except by synthesis, for the object of our service, whether an art, a profession, a country, or religion, is now bound up with that of all mankind, and we can only serve by making our own natures—mind and body—as strong and harmonious as possible. Those turning-points in human thought, of which we gave three familiar examples above, are of the greatest value which exhibit the triumph of co-operation, either in the methods of thought or the actions of men.

There are essentially two great spheres of knowledge in education—science and history. ·The other chief matters, language and mathematics, though possessing exquisite beauties of their own, are in principle instrumental to the subject-matter itself, which must be—nature and man. On both sides of this eternal dualism research has been more active and fruitful in recent years than ever. World depression, however deep it may be in the economic field, does not deter the man of science or the historian. They still bring home their sheaves rejoicing, and the only depression they create is in the mind of the anxious public and of the teachers who have somehow to digest the mass of new discoveries and prepare it for future use. Simplicity for the younger and synthesis for the older scholars are the means of safety, more necessary even in history than in natural science. For in science the success of the learner is immediately tested. The engineer has to know the calculus in order to work at all, and the physicist can at once correct his hypothesis by another experiment. But in history the results work out slowly; we have more time to think and the more need for careful thinking, because the practical test will not come at once to check us. In contemporary schools throughout the world there has been much heart-searching as to the teaching of history, more elsewhere than in England. A complete survey was organized, financed by the Carnegie Trustees, as to how history was being taught in different countries since the War, especially in reference to the national spirit displayed. The report is interesting, though not profound and far from exhaustive. The reporters find much less chauvinism than might have been expected, and a vigorous defence of the German schools was put in by Dr. Riemann, who gives copious quotations from popular books to show that the German child gets at least as fair a view of other nations as children anywhere else. He adds a well-balanced opinion of his own as to how the claims of nation and humanity should be reconciled in the teaching of the young. Both are needed, but the latter should only prevail after the child has come to know and love the land which gave him birth.

No one can read this report without feeling that, though much yet remains to be done, a new start has been made. It is not true, at any rate, that the schools of the world are more chauvinistic than before the War. No one who knows the teachers can think so. It is true that strong adverse influences still exist, mainly in the political and commercial spheres. Tariffs have risen between new states and little has been done to lower them between the old; and in certain vexed areas the grievances of minorities and the harsh measures of the majority have inflamed national passions. But teachers everywhere are a conciliatory force. They speak almost unanimously words of peace, and those who look to world co-operation as their ideal should aim, as they generally do, at enlisting the full force of the teaching profession on their side. To this end, international gatherings of teachers are becoming every year more frequent and exchanges and visits of teachers to other countries are often arranged. More potent than all this, however, would be the spread of a sounder co-operative doctrine in the schools themselves, especially in what is taught under the heading of history. It is not so much sins of commission as of omission that do the harm, or rather leave undone the good that should be done. To speak with respect of the traditions and heroes of another people is matter of common courtesy; this is being learnt to-day in popular schools, as it has always been in the more polished circles of learning or diplomacy. The more profound and necessary lesson is that the whole of history belongs to us all. It plays at present but a small part in any school curriculum, though it contains the power of combining all the rest and bringing the best of all nations into the child's consciousness.

Take, for example, the calculus which occurred above as a part of mathematics, another 'subject' in the school curriculum. That is its place as an essential tool which men have perfected for their operations on nature. But looked at from the wider point of view, as the fruit of four thousand years of human collaboration, it brings together the Egyptians, who first developed the art of measuring the soil, Greeks who analysed their methods and showed the scientific principles on which they should be based, and moderns from all the leading nations who have refined further upon the Greeks and in the end adapted to all kinds of measurements, including life and motion, the conceptions which had first arisen from the geometry of fields and stones. What to the examiner in mathematics is a section of the advanced papers, is seen to be a symbol and a summary of the progress of the human mind, sharpening its ideas through the ages and making them fitter instruments of human power in modelling the world. The scholar who realizes this has shared the mind of Archimedes, Newton, Descartes, and Leibniz, and learnt one of the most valuable lessons of history.

This, it may be said, is too hard a lesson for a child at school; that if we load history with such a burden it will break down completely. This may be true of any particular example, but we are urging a general principle which is fundamental, if the education of to-day is to become equal to the world-order of to-morrow. Any aspect of history and any period would furnish instances. Science affords the best, because it is most unquestionably co-operative and most clearly progressive; but we all might and should appreciate the Homer of the Greeks, the aqueducts of the Romans, the chivalry of the French, the music of the Germans, as well as those things—the greater mass—in in which we are all at one. Details and methods are for time and experience to settle; on the main principle both truth and humanity demand an early and decisive answer. *Elargissez l'histoire.* The demand may well seem staggering to those who think of the immensity of the realm of study which time has brought to our doors. Yet by the beneficence of nature the urgency of a case will generally bring its own redress. If we thus enlarge our conception of history and try to make it equal to its real content, the growth of the human spirit, we shall be compelled, for our own sake and for those to whom we have to transmit it, to adopt the joint method of simplification and synthesis: simplification in clearing out the dead undergrowth which obstructs the view, synthesis in concentration on those shining points in the vista of the past from which light streams on the pathway of the future.

Books for Reference

New Education Fellowship. An Introduction to the Study of Education in England and Wales. London: New Education Fellowship, 1931.

National Union of Teachers. The Hadow Report and After. London: N.U.T., 1928.

Bolton King. *Schools of To-day.* Dent.

Recent Educational Developments in Sweden. H.M. Stationery Office.

McKee. *New Schools for Young India.* Oxford University Press.

VIII

RACE PROBLEMS IN INDUSTRY AND CULTURE

By F. S. MARVIN

As this is being written, the Western world, and especially England, is being absorbed in an economic and financial crisis of which the centre lies somewhere between Paris, New York, and London, and the circumference in the ends of the earth. The centre of this aspect of the world's work has been shifting gradually for some time, and at the moment it would be difficult to say with certainty where it is, if indeed it is in any one place at all. Fifty years ago it was certainly London, because England had beaten all her rivals in maritime trade and become the pioneer in the industrial revolution. As the industrial revolution swept round the world and trade became more equally shared between the nations, London lost her pre-eminence, though for certain types of financial business London is still supreme. The volume of wealth has moved to the West, and New York, since the War, is the centre of gravity though not the centre of exchange. This gradual shifting and its cause are due to the economic development of the world stimulated by science. It cannot stop until all races are drawn into the circuit and financial direction is seen to be an international concern.

This process of world contacts between men of Western inspiration on the one hand, keen on making money and organizing in a scientific way, and the greater mass of mankind on the other hand, who had not passed through the intellectual and social upheaval of the seventeenth and eighteenth centuries, is now almost complete—in extent but not in intensity. Factories, trade relations, railways, wireless, aeroplanes, and cinemas are found in every country on earth, though their effects in many large areas are only beginning to be felt. In the wide view this must appear as the greatest revolution through which mankind has had so far to pass. We cannot yet estimate its final results, but enough has been seen to justify an interim report and suggest certain cautions.

In judging where we stand in this matter there is one almost insuperable difficulty to be met. We are bound in a summary statement to speak as if the conditions over vast tracts of land and among peoples of the most varied character and history were for the present purpose similar. We know well how different they are; the Hindu with his profound philosophy and immemorial civilization; the Chinese with their still more remote and self-centred traditions, and the host of tribes and races with no power of abstract thinking, no records of the past, no civilization above the savage. This is all patent enough, and will affect the future as it has already so notably affected the present in the case of the Japanese. Yet it must be insisted that the advent of Western science in the seventeenth century and its extension and applications ever since have created a unique division in mankind and are showing themselves, collectively, as the most important revolutionary fact in history. It is clearly apprehended as such by quick-witted nations like the Japanese, or the leaders of thought in India or China, who, not being in the movement at its inception, now take it up eagerly and use it to transform their own societies.

The Western world achieved the scientific synthesis which has proved so potent towards the end of the seventeenth century. Meanwhile, and for some time before and after, Western adventurers had been scouring the seas and making settlements in the most likely places for trade or white men's habitation. Change by contact began at once, and in the earlier stages religious conversion was directly aimed at by the Spaniards and Portuguese who felt them-

selves to be continuers of the Crusades. But by the seventeenth century relations were different between the West and
the East from what they were in the eleventh and twelfth.
The balance of knowledge was now overwhelmingly on the
Western side, which had been lagging before, and it was a
knowledge which had the power of indefinite growth. This
power began to show itself widely in the nineteenth century
at the time when the whites had established themselves
firmly in North America and gained all the commanding
positions in India and *points d'appui* in China. Since then
there has been organization and strengthening in all parts
held by the Westerner, a great reaction against Western
control in the chief centres of non-Western peoples, and an
interfusion of Western ideas everywhere. It is possible to
present a rough balance sheet, and, as always, best to put
the assets first.

First should come the fact that, wherever the Western
man has established himself in effective control, internal
peace has followed with a natural large increase in population. The acquisition of these foreign lands has been a frequent cause of war among the nations themselves, but in
the end brought peace to the conquered. Nor ought
we to reckon this the blank tragedy which the cynic pro-
claims. India is now at peace and multiplying rapidly.
The whole of Africa, which was once the scene of constant
intertribal war, is now an ordered place. No Zulu would
wish to see a Chaka again, who slew his own people by the
million; nor can we wish it for him. We may be certain,
too, that had the Westerner carried his invasion of China
as far as he carried that of India, China would not have
lost her millions by civil war and her tens of millions by
the floods. She may be gaining something more precious
in the long run, but the process is costly, and we are here
only casting up accounts to date.

On other matters, less open to mere observation or
simple numerical tests, it is not so easy to speak with

confidence. Are the non-Western races healthier, happier, more intelligent owing to their contact with the West? It is hard to find witnesses with that combination of knowledge and impartiality which would make their verdict acceptable. In India, the chief testing-ground on a large scale, rival parties for years have shouted contradictory answers without taking due account of what could be said on the other side. In China, reform leaders in recent times, while denouncing Western interference in vigorous terms, have with equal vigour declared that their country must Westernize itself completely. About Japan, opinion would probably be divided in much the same way as if we compared the England of to-day with the England of the Middle Ages. In Africa, a very able student, with opportunities of knowing both the old conditions and the new, Sir Harry Johnston, had no doubt whatever that the black population in the mass were far better off now than before the advent of the European. The balance of opinion would certainly seem to lie in that direction, after making full allowance for special vices and weakness due to Western contact. It is at least obvious that Western science and its applications are welcomed everywhere, except where such a man as Mr. Gandhi may for a time inspire opposition on national or spiritual grounds. The West gives power, and also apparently a higher degree and more varied kinds of enjoyment. This is the normal effect produced on the mind of a coloured man of any race by contact with the white man settled beside him whether for education or trade or administration, and it cannot be denied— again with all the necessary deductions—that the impression is substantially a true one. We do not ourselves propose to go back to the Middle Ages, and we should know. If we have gained on the change, is it not reasonable to expect a similar advantage to accrue to others in so far as they go through the same process? This probably is as far as the argument will take us; but one may fairly throw into the scale the many undoubted cases of advantage gained by the adoption of Western scientific methods in non-Western lands and their reconciliation with the local conditions. Success on these lines, as we shall see, points the way to the right ultimate solution of the whole problem.

But there is another side to the question which, as the West grew in power and knowledge, became increasingly evident, till now it stands in the foreground of the conscience of mankind. This is the moral aspect, which is bound to assert itself ultimately as the condition and result of all holding of power. Man is a moral being, and united as a species by innumerable links of nature and history. Hence every holder of exceptional power has felt some sense of duty towards those dependent on him; at the best, as in the Golden Age of the Roman Empire, men have risen on this basis to be the noblest examples of human nature. Such power is now unattainable by individuals and lies in associations of men. Such an association in the British Empire became conscious of its power and its attendant duty towards the end of the eighteenth century. Burke's assertion of the principle in the trial of Warren Hastings is one of the turning-points in modern history; less on account of its immediate occasion than as the voice of the triumphant West accepting for the future a new line of conduct for all dominant powers. This principle of trusteeship, of the stronger for the weaker, has been applied, imperfectly no doubt, but with growing steadiness throughout the nineteenth century, and is now embodied in international law in the Covenant of the League of Nations.

It is a common but superficial fallacy to ignore or belittle the non-material and non-legal factors in the make-up of civilization. They always tend to be so belittled just as they are making their way in the world. No one would be so foolish as to think of a father's tie to his children as

limited only by his legal obligations, nor would any student
of history deny the gradual evolution of the paternal
relation, both on the legal and the moral side. This
advance in the moral sphere is now so firmly established
that no one questions it, but a similar evolution may be
traced, from the semi-savage—say the Assyrian stage—in
which the conquered are treated as the mere tools or
chattels of the conqueror, to the relation contemplated in
the Mandate system by which the stronger Power, finding
itself in a position of control, is bound to use that position
for the education and advancement of the weaker subordinate, and give an account of this trusteeship to the
authorized tribunal of mankind. Both evolutions, though
unlike in detail and in the personal tie, are equally real and
in the same direction, of enforcing by the moral sense and
by human sympathy the duty of using superior strength
for the advancement of the weaker and the general good
of all.

The period since the War has seen a notable advance in
the international position, both of the smaller nations
generally and also of those communities which have more
lately entered the orbit of Western civilization. The former
entered at once into full membership of the League
of Nations on an equal basis in the Assembly with the
strongest Powers. The latter either entered at once, like
India and China, or have been gradually coming in as their
governments became settled or as they are released from
their tutelage under the Mandates system. Thus a steady
flow is going on in the direction of giving more weight
in world affairs to the interests of the smaller and rising
peoples and less to those of mere power and wealth. All
this is to the advantage of the cause of humanity, widely
and justly considered, and it brings into a state of friendly
co-operation nations of the most diverse strength and
degrees of civilization. It is the natural process of education. Sweden, for instance, stands by universal consent in

the foremost rank of civilized peoples, while Abyssinia is
on the fringe and still contains multitudes of slaves. Both,
however, would be in the same class as smaller Powers, and
would doubtless be found in the same lobby on a division
involving the rights of the weak against the strong. Year
by year this balance will be strengthened as fresh junior
nations arrive. Iraq and Mexico are received to-day, and
to-morrow Egypt, Syria, and Palestine will be knocking at
the door. The prospect is entirely normal and satisfactory,
granted only that the stronger Powers abstain, or are
restrained, from grouping round themselves a string of
satellites, and granted also that they play their part in
conducting general affairs in the general interest. It
is clearly to the general interest that the process of en-
franchisement should go on and the circle of civilized and
self-conscious nations be enlarged. Great Britain, France,
and Holland are now the Western Powers with the largest
control of backward peoples; Belgium, with her Congo, is a
rapidly improving fourth. In all these cases, and especially
in that of Great Britain and Holland, the post-War time
has brought a marked advance in the status of the subject
peoples.

So far we have been considering the brighter side of the
picture; it is time now to turn to the difficulties and dangers
of the contact and explore for a little the possible means by
which the good sense and humanity of mankind may overcome them. The illustrations given must be necessarily
partial and come mainly from South Africa; so far as may
be, those points will be chosen which might *mutatis
mutandis* be applied elsewhere.

The effects of the contact of stronger and more advanced
peoples on weaker and more primitive must be felt on both
sides, but the weaker will take the deeper imprint. For
them it is a revolution unprepared for; in any case they
have not been through the long scientific evolution which
was of capital importance in the West; in many cases, as

with the aborigines of Australia or Central Africa, they are still in the earliest stage of conscious thought. The plunge therefore, if they survive it, is a complete change of their mental outlook and habits. In many cases it has meant extinction; in many others the almost total loss of their old attachments and sanctions without the acquisition of any solid new foundations. This is so familiar a case all over the world that it hardly needs illustration. Many primitive races have in this manner disappeared, and others are in course of doing so. Diseases of sex and alcoholism have also been rife among such people, due directly or indirectly to European influence. Where European governments are in command steps are now being taken to check these more deadly evils; on the west coast of Africa, for instance, the most elaborate regulations are in force for the control of the liquor traffic, and the same question exercises the South African governments.

Larger, if not so acute, problems arise in the case of those—the large majority—who show no sign of succumbing physically to Western contact. This is the general case in Africa, where the negro race, in spite of manifold disease, is vigorous and multiplying. It is with the living and not the dying that the white man has to deal in the new century, and, though we must deplore and do our utmost to prevent the physical decadence of any race over which we have the responsibility of government, it seems to be a law of nature that certain races die out from the mere presence of others physically stronger than themselves.

It is, of course, with the negro race, strong and increasing, that the chief problems arise both in Africa and the New World, and one can only on so vast a subject select one or two points which seem to have most bearing on a new world-order.

To the various Bantu tribes of the negro race, with whom the white settlers in South and East Africa have to do, the white invasion has not brought extinction, or even, so far as we can judge, any impairment of vitality; but it has brought large dispossession from the lands which they held, rather loosely, before our advent; great changes in their tribal life, and a keen and increasing competition in the field of modern industry with white workers in those parts where white men can make a permanent home.

The whites also suffer damage in another way, and, if we are to judge the whole question fairly, we must take account of this as well. It was an old black wag who said, 'Before you came we had the land and you had the Bible. Now you have the land and we the Bible.' The judgement was humorous, but it contains some truth. The material gain has been almost entirely on the side of the invader, but material gain in such conditions tends to bring some loss. It is loss and not gain if we acquire the habit of having all manual and menial work done for us by others of a race which we consider inferior. It was contempt such as this which brought down the old Greco-Roman world and prevented the brilliance of Greek science from having its natural fruits in industry. Moreover, to limit our view by an irrational prejudice against colour, as such, is to penalize ourselves even more seriously than the Greeks. For they had no such prejudice, and the Hellenization of the Middle West, which was the social advantage of Alexander's conquest, was due to an amalgamation of blood as well as culture. The same thing was true of the Roman Empire, and, though these cases should by no means determine so vexed a question, it is well to know and record the facts.

One obvious result, evil for all parties, which meets the inquirer in South Africa is the production of a large class of 'poor whites', men brought up with no capacity for the manual labour by which they might live, and who have to be maintained at the cost of the community, either by pure charity or by paying an eleemosynary and uneconomic wage for work which might be better done by the despised black.

It is of course clear that arrangements such as these are bound to give way to the demands both of economy and of common sense, to say nothing of humanity. In the new age all men are demanding the opportunities which education may give them, and, subject to capacity and educated skill, the right to equal treatment before the law and a fair remuneration for their labour, irrespective of colour or race. No one stands to lose by this, because the increase of educated capacity must give a greater market for all sorts of products. The change will come gradually and there is no fear of violence or revolution; but the white man has definitely to put out of his mind the idea of the black (or of any colour) as a race destined by nature to work for his convenience whenever fate should bring them together. The notion has been expelled from the centre of civilization, where, as at Geneva, black, white, and yellow sit side by side on the Assembly benches; but it lingers long in the extremities, and is stronger among Anglo-Saxons and the vigorous races of northern blood than among more Southern people.

The point is fundamental but curiously misunderstood. When speaking, as here, of the need of regarding the black man as a fellow citizen with rights of his own, and not as a mere instrument for the profit of the white, one is often met by the rejoinder, 'But do you then advocate a complete mixture of races?' The two questions are entirely independent. Miscegenation may, or may not, be desirable, according to circumstances and to the teachings of biology. The best opinion and certainly current inclination seem tending against it at the present time. People of different blood seem more anxious to preserve it pure than they used to be. But the doctrine of common citizenship is a human and general thing going back to Kant and the Revolution, if not to the Stoics, and made possible

and necessary in practice to-day by the unification of the
world and the League of Nations. It is not too much to
say that all the problems of race contact in such countries
as South or East Africa, where white and black are settling
down permanently side by side, require for their solution
a recognition of this principle as the preliminary, and that,
when it is recognized, the problem is more than half
solved. Until South Africa can not only contemplate, but
insist on having, a Bantu as one of its delegation to Geneva,
it has not recognized the principle.

The circumstances of South Africa are so interesting and
illustrate so many aspects of the problem of race contacts,
that they must be given in somewhat more detail than any
other case we can mention. It seems in fact to be an
example of that *experimentum crucis* of the old philosophers which will show the world whether human intelligence and good-will are sufficient to solve the problem
in a decisive case. For in South Africa one has all the
difficulties in full force. But two main factors point to a
successful issue; on the one side marked patience to good
temper in the mass of the population; on the other, proved
success of the British in similar cases, of which Jamaica is
the nearest parallel.

In the first place, then, both races—for obviously from
this point of view Boer and British must be treated as
one—are permanently in the field together. Neither white
nor black has any intention of leaving the country. For
two million of the former and eight million of the latter it
is a home, and shows every sign of remaining one. Clearly,
therefore, the South African nation is both black and
white, and if we represent it by a piece of striped material,
the black stripes are four times as wide as the white. But
we must add to this first numerical comparison a second.
The black majority before the advent of the whites roamed
over and slightly cultivated the whole area; and for the
purpose of this comparison one may fairly include among

the majority the bushmen and Hottentots who have now dwindled to an insignificant minority. The blacks now possess land in almost exactly the inverse ratio to their numbers. Being four times as many as the whites, they have one-fourth of the land. Clearly again, this dispossession and the large loss of their old tribal holdings must have brought great changes in their mode of life. Either they must have become impoverished, or they must have improved their methods of cultivation, or they must have found other sources of livelihood. The last method of the three has been far the most operative. Work on the mines, or other form of service for the whites, has come in to eke out their scanty means and maintain their numbers. It is calculated that 75 per cent. of the adult black population in the Union have at some time taken work on the mines and quite half go regularly either there or to some other industrial employment every year and take back savings to their homesteads.

There is a curious analogy between the remuneration gained by whites and blacks at the two main forms of labour open to them. It is found that, owing to their superior organization and the use of agricultural machinery and scientific methods, the white man is able to make six times as much out of his land as the black cultivator. At the same time the wage paid to the white and black in industry is also roughly as six to one. Here are the broad facts and they suggest one or two reflections, again necessarily of a general kind. Firstly, it must be held right, in accordance with Lord Lugard's principles in his *Dual Mandate in Africa*, that more return should be sought from the soil than is possible by the primitive methods of native cultivation. It would not have been right, or possible in view of the increasing population of the globe, to leave its surface undisturbed in the hands of its primitive holders. Man has a duty towards the earth as well as to his fellow men. But it is not sufficient to dispossess these primitive holders and take it all into more competent hands. An advance must be made all along the line, among the cultivators as well as in the cultivation. Unfortunately the former process is much slower and more difficult than the latter. Something has been done, but, as the interest of the large white landholder is more involved in maintaining his large holdings with a good supply of cheap labour, the process of improving the black cultivator working for himself is apt to lag behind. Agricultural training places for the natives are spreading over South Africa, and they are eagerly attended. In Bechuanaland and the Transkei most advance appears to have been made. The black farmer is being taught to improve his cattle and make more use of them. In some cases he is reported to have made saleable butter, though not yet cheese. This is a Western art well taught to a man who has been content for generations to make a living on a patch of mealies and accumulate, as wealth, a herd of scraggy and unprofitable beasts.

But any changes must come slowly, and wholesome social changes more slowly than the bad. The problem is one of education in the widest sense. As the black cultivator becomes more generally intelligent and competent, his powers both of production and of enjoyment will increase. His earnings and his consumption are at present below the scale, not only of his real capacity but of his actual needs, and to lessen the gap which divides him from the white man would be to the advantage of all.

So much is clear on general grounds, but the question is complicated in South Africa and elsewhere by a multitude of puzzling local conditions. At present in a large number of cases the wages earned in industry are a supplement to the scanty livelihood afforded by the plot of land at home. As agricultural methods improve and if more land could be provided—a long-crying need not yet satisfied—the home farm would become the natural and sufficient sustenance for the family, and those going into industry would

tend more and more to be the younger members of the
family, and look to their industrial remuneration for their
own complete support. Both types would become more
self-sufficient, and, with the gradual working out of the
mines, the agricultural section become again, in an enlarged and revitalized form, the normal type. So far as
industrial wages are concerned it is impossible to justify
on any grounds the yawning gulf between the white man's
£1 a day and the black man's £4 a month. It is not necessary to level up entirely, for the different standards of
comfort are still too far apart. But some approximation
is called for, and, as things now are and for a long time
ahead, the natural place of the white workman is in
positions of supervision and organization. As education
makes the others more capable, there can be no reason why
men of any colour should not do work of any kind for
which individually they are most fit.

Education, therefore, as Professor Julian Huxley reminds us in his recent book on East Africa,[1] is the high
road to all advance. Happily the best way to educate is
now being closely studied in many centres in South Africa
and all over the world where Western men are in contact
with primitive peoples. The faults of the past are generally
recognized, but this is easier than seeing the right way to
do the work in future. Most difficult of all is to secure the
force of enlightened, sympathetic, and effective teachers
who could do over vast tracts of the earth's surface what
Mr. McKee did for one district in the Punjab. One or two
general remarks may do something to clear up our own
ideas on the subject and link it up with the main theme of
this book.

There is now a strong reaction in theory against exces-
sive Westernizing and, still more, Anglicizing the education
of the primitive. We can all see the absurdity of teaching
the young Bantu the flowers in an English garden or the

[1] *Africa View.* Chatto & Windus.

L

provisions of the Constitution of Clarendon, but when his teachers go on to say, as they often do, that his education should be entirely African, one fears the customary swing of the pendulum. A purely African education would not suit the new world order any better than a purely Asiatic or a purely Russian. The common things in education, as in life, are the more important and, even with our growing freedom and individuality, they, too, are growing in importance. This is true of language, as well as of science and mathematics, and it should be truer than it is of history. It is rather the colour than the substance of his education which should be African, like the African's skin which covers a common structure and a common heart. Thus—to put the matter definitely—the laws of thought, which we call mathematics, and the laws of nature, which we call science, are identical for all men, and there is a marked tendency in recent years, in spite of nationalism, to simplify and unify our means of communication by language and otherwise. Smaller languages are dying out and great languages, especially English, are spreading. We must aim at giving the young Bantu the benefit of this common heritage of mankind, if he is to be a fit member of his nation. These common fundamentals should not obstruct or destroy the other side, or colour, of his education which springs from his own surroundings and his racial tradition. Thus his art would be different and his local geography and natural history, while the ideal for him, and for others, is to have one natural or domestic language and another for intercourse with the outside world and the great thoughts of the past.

It may be thought that we are painting a picture on too ideal lines and that practical work, such as Mr. McKee carried out at Moga, is much more suited to native needs. But this is a question of methods and not of ideals. Practical work on the Moga lines—carpentry, farming, dispensing and the like—have proved themselves everywhere to be effective methods of rousing the interests of the young, especially of those who do not start their education in a cultured sphere. The special value of his experiment was its demonstration that by these means a powerful stimulus can be given to the whole life of a countryside, stirring up its people to make more use of their opportunities, to face nature with more skilled weapons and act more heartily in co-operation with their neighbours. But at the basis of all this lies the acquisition of the common methods of human thought involved in simple mathematics, and the faithful observation of the laws of nature which have given the Western world the mighty instrument of science. So that, however carefully we may preserve the local atmosphere of any people, the main result of contact in education must be assimilation. Nor ought we to recoil from this, for the great principle of 'unity in diversity' must govern between races and nations as between the individuals in any nation.

There are still wider issues involved in this contact of races throughout the world which some writers have discussed under the superficial and forbidding titles of the 'Clash of Colour' or the 'Yellow Peril', and so on. 'Colour' is not the danger, but low standards of living and thinking on the one side and selfishness on the other. They can only be met by humane and scientific education in the first case and the sincere acceptance of the ideal of a united humanity in the second. It has been seen in earlier chapters that the world has by now given lip-service to these ideals in all its public utterances. For that reason, and for the real advance already made, we are justified in speaking of a 'new order'. But a long road yet remains to traverse before the home-coming can be safely reckoned on, and there are some ugly corners to turn. Some of them touch on parts of the Anglo-Saxon world, or the British Commonwealth, which justly boasts of wise and successful action in many places. It is far more useful to think of such definite

sore places and how to cure them, than to alarm ourselves
vaguely about a 'clash of colour' which, as a general fact,
does not exist. But there does exist a teeming population
in Japan, pressing for outlets, and hundreds of millions of
Chinese, kept down at present by the ravages of mis-
government. India, too, constantly increases her needy
but industrious and naturally skilful peasantry. Meanwhile the white man in Australia, South Africa, and on
the Pacific coast is maintaining in his own supposed
interest the strictest exclusion that he can arrange against
the settlement of these people in lands which he controls
and they could happily and profitably inhabit. It is a
policy untenable in the long run, condemned alike by considerations of industry, biology, and humanity. Let us be
thankful that a League of Nations stands in the breach,
prepared not yet to take active steps, for other more urgent
tasks are still in hand, but to keep steadily before the eyes
of all parties the hopes and duties of co-operating mankind.

BOOKS FOR REFERENCE

Sir Harry Johnston. *Black and White in Africa*. Oxford University
    Press.
Julian Huxley. *Africa View*. Chatto & Windus.
Lord Lugard. *The Dual Mandate in Africa*.
Toynbee. *Survey of International Affairs, passim*. Oxford Uni-
    versity Press.

IX

RECENT DEVELOPMENTS IN INTER-
NATIONAL LAW[1]

By ÖSTEN UNDÉN

I INTEND to deal with questions that do not all belong to
'international law' in a more limited and technical sense.
I have first some brief general observations to make about
the fundamental problem of the possibility and the importance of an international organization, aiming at the
safeguarding of peace and the establishment and maintenance of the rule of law in the relationship of States. This
problem might be called a problem of international constitutional law as it concerns the form of international
government, and its most important, immediate aspect is
that regarding the League of Nations. International law
in the wider sense, I take it, here includes also the rules
of procedure applied in disputes between States, i.e. the
organization of international arbitration. And, finally, I
have to make some remarks on what might be characterized as the common or civil international law, especially
the question of its codification. I must, of course, confine
myself to the general tendencies prevailing in these large
domains of international organization and law-making.

During the last decades our conception of the social
world and our view of international relationship have been
decidedly altered. A more scientific method in the consideration of our social life, including our international
relations, appears to be gradually making headway. As
an American author has pointed out, this method signifies
that we replace *tradition* with *purpose*, i.e. we value the
institutions of the commonwealth not according to their
historical age and usage, but according to their practica-
bility at the present time and for the future.

[1] The lecture is published here in abbreviated form.

In no field is perhaps the need of new methods and of new tendencies more acute in our day than in the field of international politics and law, i.e. when the issue concerns the relationship between various countries. The meaning of a world war and its consequences are still vivid in our minds. Another catastrophe of the same magnitude would perhaps mean the destruction of our culture. No mission can be more important than to establish a real international organization. The generation that lived during the War, and those conscious of its effects, ought to feel the special responsibility devolving upon them to contribute to a development in this direction.

How was the problem of peace regarded prior to the world war? In leading political and diplomatic circles, the world over, war has at best appeared as a natural force which human intelligence and energy cannot resist. Some thought that perhaps it might be worth while to direct all efforts towards putting off for a brief period the inevitable catastrophe. Others were of the opinion that, as far as their country was concerned, a postponement would do more harm than good. But irrespective of one opinion or the other, the real aim of the politics of the leading countries was to strengthen their position in a future war by means of armaments and alliances. A problem of peace and international organization hardly existed in the sense of nations and their statesmen directing their efforts towards controlling the natural forces that threatened to bring about war.

The question can now be asked: Are any new tendencies really being felt in international politics in our day?

So far as I can see, an effort is noticeable everywhere to consider the problem of peace as a problem of inter-national organization, that should be capable of solution by rational methods as other social problems are being solved. The existence of the League of Nations is, in my mind, the most significant expression of this new policy. The opinion is growing that peace can and must be secured by other methods than those of armaments and alliances in the old traditional way.

When the League of Nations and its importance are discussed, the question is often raised as to its present strength and value in the event of a serious crisis in foreign politics. Naturally, this question is difficult to answer definitely. After all, the main problem is this: Is the League founded on sound and correct principles, and is the future of the League assured? In my personal opinion there is no doubt in this respect. The only way to organize peace methodically and rationally is to unite the various countries in an organization that will, on the one hand, offer the means and agencies of dealing with the different questions that produce conflicts between nations, and, on the other hand, will intervene with appropriate methods of pressure against an aggressor, and thus guarantee a certain amount of protection to the members of the League. It is difficult to think of any other way of securing a state of law and peace than that of international co-operation within a mutual and permanent organization of governments, just as peace and order within the countries have been established through improved organization and the development of a system of law. And every such system inevitably demands certain restrictions on the sovereignty or the liberty of action of the individual States.

The League of Nations is a constitutional novelty. Its foundation may be considered as the starting-point for the development of a constitutional and administrative international law. The League is no 'superstate'; that is true Its assembly and other organs have not yet any real legislative functions identical with those attributed to Parliaments; the League is an embryo that may in the future grow to a sort of federative commonwealth with certain legislative attributions.

The *method* of international legislation differs very considerably from the method of municipal legislation. As an international legislature is lacking we have to proceed by means of international treaties. But such a treaty binds only those States which have signed and ratified the treaty. Theoretically, at least, no State can be obliged to accept a new rule that it does not approve. If there is a need for a legislative measure within the domain of international law, the only practical method is therefore to invite the governments to send delegates to an international conference that can deal with the problem, and try to make a unanimously accepted draft-treaty, that later on may be ratified by the different governments.

It is evident that this machinery is not very satisfactory unless there is a central authority to convoke the conference, prepare its work, and insist upon the ratification of the adopted draft-treaties. A certain number of law-making conferences were held during the nineteenth century; but the initiative usually fell to some single State and the attempts were isolated. In some special and limited fields a kind of international union was established whereby the continuance of the legislative work was secured.

After the foundation of the League of Nations it was possible to approach the development of international legislation with renewed energy. An agency, a permanent machinery for assembling international conferences and for facilitating their negotiations, has finally come into existence. The Assembly of the League is in itself a periodical meeting of representatives of the Powers capable of negotiating treaties. The Assembly has, for instance, elaborated the statute of the Permanent Court of International Justice and the General Act of Arbitration, though the preparatory work was accomplished by commissions of experts. Other organs of the League, the International Labour Office and the Labour Conferences, have been continuously or periodically occupied with international legislative measures within the scope of the labour problems. Besides, the League very often summons special conferences for dealing with important legislative questions. In these cases, too, the secretariat of the League acts as an agency, enabling the conference to work effectively when once assembled.

A radical change in method has thus taken place, promising to be of a far-reaching influence upon the development of international law.

I pass now to another domain where very important results have been reached during the last ten years, I mean the international arbitration system. We have now arrived at a sort of international law of procedure for the use of the States. There is also another set of rules that is denominated international law of procedure, but in this connexion I am referring to procedure rules concerning the dealing with disputes between governments, not between individuals.

You know certainly the outstanding facts: namely, the establishment of the Permanent Court of International Justice and the conclusion of a great number of arbitration treaties, binding the signatory Powers to submit all international disputes or all such disputes of a juridical nature to the Permanent Court or to a tribunal of arbitration. It is not an exaggeration to say that the progress made in this domain signifies a new era in international relations. The importance of the arbitration settlements cannot be measured by the number of cases that are actually brought before the Court or an arbitral tribunal. The effect of the stipulations is, above all, that governments may be expected to be more reasonable and to execute their obligations more willingly if they know that the other party can always refer the dispute to an international court and obtain a judgement.

I beg you to reflect upon the functions and the effects of the ordinary tribunals within a country. Suppose that we had in Sweden a great body of laws concerning different matters, as contracts and torts and ownership, &c., but no rules of procedure and no tribunals to which disputes could be referred. Do you think it likely that we should make much use of the laws under such circumstances? For my part I think not. If there were no tribunals in Sweden with power to deal with disputes between the inhabitants we would perhaps be inclined to say that Sweden possessed no real system of law. The tribunals are an essential part of a system of law and order. Without them legal rules would very often not be applied at all, or they would be applied in an arbitrary way.

Now, if you consider the law of nations as it existed before the establishment of any compulsory jurisdiction, you will find a certain number of rules, adopted by international conventions, or by the practice of the governments, or recognized in arbitration sentences. The existence of these rules has no doubt been of a certain value, and it has often happened that governments have agreed to let a special arbitration commission or tribunal decide a dispute by the application of those recognized rules. But in every case of this kind it has been necessary for the applicant to obtain the assent of the other party as to the submission of the dispute to the international tribunal. You realize at once what a difference there is when a government is entitled to get a juridical dispute settled by an international tribunal without the assent of the defendant State.

The machinery for settling international disputes by arbitration has, consequently, been very much developed during the last years. The institution of the Permanent Court of International Justice is the work of the League. The statute of the Court was elaborated by a League Commission and adopted by the Assembly in 1921, and the League has to elect the members of the Court and pay the cost of its functioning. The statute of the Court signifies at the same time an international treaty between the signatory Powers. The adhesion to the statute need not, however, involve the adoption of compulsory jurisdiction. But there is in the statute the well-known optional clause in art. 36, § 2, that permits States to adhere to a special protocol providing for compulsory jurisdiction in all disputes of a legal character. A large number of States have given their signature to this special protocol and thus adopted compulsory jurisdiction in their mutual relations.

Besides, we have now many bilateral arbitration treaties and, at last, the General Act of 1928 that is intended to be a codification of the whole arbitration system and to make bilateral conventions superfluous in the future.

However important this development of international jurisdiction may be, you must not suppose that the arbitration treaties provide for settlement of all kinds of disputes, and that the tribunals or the Court have jurisdiction in every possible case of disputes likely to disturb the peaceful relations between States. The tribunals have a judicial function; they are not intended to be a substitute for a legislative agency. They shall pronounce their judgements on the basis of existing international law, but if the existing treaties and other legal rules are unsatisfactory the tribunals are unable to deal with the real causes of the dispute. I shall take an example: the conclusion of a commercial treaty is not a question that may be referred to an international tribunal. But its negotiation may very well lead to a state of international tension. Another example: according to recognized international law, the question of minorities is a domestic question, falling solely within every State's own jurisdiction, except in cases when a State has assumed special obligations by signing a minority treaty. It may very well happen, however, that the treatment of a minority population in a country that has not signed a minority treaty is such as to raise difficulties with a neighbouring State. The dispute arising out of the treatment of the minority cannot then be settled by an international tribunal according to the usual arbitration treaties. If the case is brought before the tribunal the result will be only a sentence that declares what is international law in the matter, and consequently confirms the liberty of action of the defendant State.

You may object that there are a certain number of arbitration treaties that provide also for the settlement of non-legal disputes, so called political disputes, for instance the General Act of 1928. But it was not intended by the authors of this Act to give the arbitral tribunals power to revise existing treaties or pronounce sentences contrary to established international law. There is, however, a method of dealing with questions which may be said to involve something of a legislative nature. The commissions of conciliation, instituted according to arbitration treaties of the Locarno-type, or in conformity with the General Act, are entitled to examine all international problems without exception. And so is the Council of the League of Nations in cases where such a dispute may be considered as a menace to peace.

There is still this difference between the recommendations of the Council or of a commission of conciliation and the sentence of a tribunal, that the latter contains a definite and binding decision, while the former are only propositions which the parties may reject. It must thus be admitted that there is no appropriate machinery in existence for legislative measures in international questions that can be compared with the parliaments and governments as agencies for municipal law-making.

As I pointed out at the beginning, progress has been made not only in constitutional law and in the law of procedure, but also in the field of what I have called common international law. The expression is not adequate, but I use it for the sake of convenience.

The progress made in this domain concern the material contents of the international rules that determine the rights and obligations of States.

A highly important example of international legislation in this sense is the conclusion of the already-mentioned minority conventions in connexion with certain transfers of territories according to the Peace treaties. I do not intend to explain here the contents of these various conventions. I only wish to emphasize that the provisions concerning international guarantees for the protection of minorities signify that these delicate questions have become, to a certain extent, questions of a legal nature, that may be referred to the Permanent Court for decision.

While most minority treaties were drafted and signed before the definite foundation of the League, there is another important group of treaties of a legislative nature that has been framed by organs of the League. I mean the already-mentioned labour conventions. The difficulties of getting these draft treaties adopted by the States have no doubt been very great. The most important of them all—the Eight Hours Convention—is still ratified only by a rather limited number of governments. But the existence of the International Labour Organization as an agency of the League of Nations is a significant symptom of the social needs of our time, and may be of far-reaching importance in future.

A great number of law-making treaties of a humanitarian, economic, or technical character have been concluded with the assistance of the League's organs. Naturally, the efforts have not always been successful. The existing legislative machinery in the international field is very imperfect, as I have already pointed out, and it is not surprising that a conference sometimes has ended in failure.

Some years ago a resolution was passed by the Assembly

to the effect that a commission of jurists should prepare
a more systematic examination of subjects fit for regulation by international agreement. The initiative in this
matter was given by the Swedish Government. The under-
lying idea was that future attempts to make adequate the
law of nations are not to depend on chance, they ought
to be the result of a deliberated and planned course of
action.

The Commission selected by the Council of the League
had a rather limited task. It had not to draft any definite
new provisions, it had only to prepare a provisional list of
the subjects of international law, the regulation of which
would seem to be most desirable at the present moment.
The Commission of Codification—as it was denominated—
has accomplished a valuable preparatory work and pre-
sented to the Council a list of subjects considered as
sufficiently ripe for legislation. The first Conference of
Codification was held in 1930. Three important problems
were put on the agenda: the question of territorial waters,
the question of responsibility of States for injuries to aliens,
and certain questions of nationality. Unfortunately, the
result of this Conference was not very satisfactory. It was
impossible to reach unanimous solutions of the principal
problems under discussion. The conflicting interests were
too great.

It may be remembered, in this connexion, that the
jurisprudence of the Permanent Court has contributed, to
a considerable extent, to the development of international
law. Several judgements and advisory opinions of the
Court constitute precedents of the highest importance for
the application of existing law.

I shall now end·my short observations concerning recent
developments in international law with the hope that you
realize what important progress has been made during the
last decade. The progress already made does encourage us
to believe that the prospect for international law in our

century is promising. The success depends ultimately upon the creative spirit, and especially the co-operative efforts, of the young generation in the different countries.

BOOKS FOR REFERENCE

J. W. Wheeler Bennett and M. Fanshawe. *Information on the World Court, 1918–28*. Allen & Unwin, 1929.

J. L. Brierly., *The Law of Nations*. Oxford University Press, 1928.

C. Howard Ellis. *The Origin, Structure, and Working of the League of Nations*, chapters ix and x. Allen & Unwin, 1928.

M. O. Hudson. 'The Development of International Law since the War.' Reprinted from *The American Journal of International Law*. April 1928.

Sir J. Fischer Williams. *International Change and International Peace*. Oxford University Press, 1932.

—— *Chapters on Current International Law and the League of Nations*. Longmans, 1929.

For books of all sizes and scope in connexion with this chapter refer to the Library of the League of Nations Union, 15 Grosvenor Crescent, S.W. 1.

X

ECONOMIC SUCCESS AND FAILURE

By HARTLEY WITHERS

NOTHING has more clearly shown the interdependence of the nations, and the unity of mankind in its material interests, than the economic experiences of the post-War period.

In the century before the War immense progress had been made in the production and distribution of the good things that we all want to enjoy, as improved means of transport and communication knit all the world more closely together into one great market, fed and supplied by a growing stream of commodities and services. In England, where the new industrial system had had its earliest development, a rapid growth in population had been accompanied by such a still more rapid growth in industrial achievement, that it was stated by Sir Josiah Stamp, in a book published in 1922, that 'the ordinary person of to-day is four times as well off in real commodities as the person in the corresponding stage in the scale in the beginning of the nineteenth century', and that 'the evidence goes to show that this increase has been evenly shared by all classes of the population'.

Improvement must have been even more rapid in the United States, where a vast area, teeming with a great variety of natural resources, was being harnessed for production by a highly enterprising population, assisted by a stream of capital and immigrants from England and Europe. All over the world the process of development was going on through the co-operation of the old and settled countries with the newer nations that were breaking up fresh soil for productive use. England was pouring capital and immigrants into America and into her Dominions, and the export of capital from France, Germany, Holland, and the Scandinavian countries was helping to promote the growth of production in Latin America, Russia, Asia, and the more backward parts of Europe.

These developments had been inevitably marked by ugly features on which there is no need to dwell here; and they had been accompanied by the growth of tendencies which threatened to limit their successful continuance, chief among which was the desire of the new countries to foster, by tariffs and other artificial means, their power to produce not only the food and materials that they exchanged with the manufactures of the industrialized nations, but finished articles turned out by their own factories. But by and large the century before the War showed us what the world could do when it gave free play, unhindered by international strife and jealousies, to man's natural instinct to make and grow things and exchange them with his neighbours. Helped by the discoveries of science and the ingenuity of inventors, and working on the materials that the new countries poured out, the old countries supplied the new with capital and equipment which enabled the latter to reach in a few years a level of comfort which Europe had taken centuries to achieve, and in many cases to surpass it. This stream of new capital was not, of course, always well used, and grave mistakes were often made, for which both lenders and borrowers were responsible; but the development of the international capital market, based on mutual confidence in political stability and the fulfilment of contracts, spread a fertilizing stream over all the world which immensely quickened its power to produce and enjoy a growing stream of material comfort with all the possibilities of higher civilization which material comfort brings with it.

Into this complicated and delicate mechanism of international credit, based on confidence and stability, the War crashed like a bombshell into a cucumber frame shattering it to pieces. For the time the world gave all its attention

M

to producing weapons of destruction and to providing food and equipment, on a scale hitherto undreamt of, for immense numbers of the flower of the human race engaged on the task of mutual extermination. Science and invention were chiefly concentrated in perfecting and devising weapons and killing apparatus; but at the same time the quickened demand for food and materials brought large new areas under cultivation and also promoted the application of science to the production and transport of useful commodities.

At the end of the War the world thus found itself with its distribution of wealth profoundly altered and a great growth in productive power hampered by the impoverishment of the area, Europe, which had hitherto been most important to civilization, and the break-up of the old system of co-operation and exchange of commodities. We shall see that its task of getting back to, and then improving on, the old system that had done so much in the previous century was crowned with success so far as it was approached through methods of co-operation, and has been reduced to tragic and ridiculous failure owing to neglect of these methods and the cultivation of the spirit of economic nationalism.

Looking first at the success side of the balance sheet, it can certainly be claimed that Europe did, for a time, manage to secure what seemed to be a remarkable triumph over the difficulties inflicted upon her by the dislocation of her industries and trade, by the erection, by the Treaty of Versailles, of a number of new States, all of which eagerly applied their new-found sovereignty to the effort to keep one another's goods out, and by the chaos into which their budgets and currencies had been reduced by the War's effects. Formerly a provider of capital, she now found herself in need of it for purposes of reconstruction. England, the chief lender before the War, had her own domestic needs to meet and was saving less owing to after-

War taxation and other causes. America had leapt at one
bound from the position of a debtor country to that of
creditor of all the world, and was more than ready, with
charitable effort and with the provision of capital, to
remedy the effects of the struggle which she had so
efficiently helped to end. But capital will only follow
confidence; and it was not until the League of Nations had
taken the reconstruction of Austria in hand, and produced
a workable scheme for the balancing of her budget and the
stabilization of her currency, that the work of European
reconstruction could begin with a loan to Austria,
guaranteed chiefly by England, France, Italy, and Czechoslovakia, and subscribed by American, British, and continental investors. Germany, where the use of the printing
press had divided the value of the mark by millions, was
set on her feet financially by measures taken by the
victorious Powers anxious to put her in a position to pay
Reparations, and endorsed by America, which took part in
the framing and execution of the Dawes and Young Plans,
both of which were named after prominent Americans.
France, whose franc had fallen to one-fifth of its pre-War
exchange value, rescued her finances and stabilized her
franc by her own exertions as soon as M. Poincaré had
succeeded, by statesmanlike measures, in restoring the
confidence of Frenchmen in their country's financial
position.

While these successes were being secured in the domain
of international and governmental finance, it is highly
satisfactory to note that there had been a considerable
improvement in the distribution of wealth and in the attention given to the social services.

In England, though as the chief international trader she
had suffered more than any other nation from the after-
War dislocation of commerce, real wages (that is money
wages considered in relation to purchasing power), had
shown a considerable advance in the case of unskilled

workers and had been maintained in that of other wage-earners at a time when the incomes of other classes, especially those of the very rich, had been drastically reduced by the severity of direct taxation. And in addition to this absolute and relative improvement in the wage-earners' income, expenditure on the social services—health, education, unemployment insurance, &c.—had received an addition of over £300 millions as compared with its figure in pre-War times. Moreover, impoverished as the Continent was, this improvement in the lot of those who do the hardest work had been, in varying degrees, general throughout its area.

In America a new era appeared to have dawned, in which all the world's most difficult economic problems had been solved or were in process of solution. Manufacturers, led by Mr. Henry Ford, had discovered that high wages mean increased purchasing power, among a great number of customers, for mass-produced goods, and in varying degrees the whole country was enjoying unparalleled prosperity, with high wages, high profits, and an immense and growing consumption of goods poured out by skilfully mechanized industry at prices which were stable or slightly cheaper, this consumption being quickened by the development of the system of purchases by instalment payments.

World trade, though hampered by economic nationalism which obstructed it by means of new and higher tariff barriers, nevertheless succeeded in growing, thanks to the desire of all countries to export, a desire which they can only satisfy if at the same time they import something—goods or services and promises to pay—and thanks also to the partial revival of the international capital market by foreign investments carried out chiefly by America and England. The growth of international trade was not as rapid as that of the general productive power; and England's position, with her special dependence on world trade for the prosperity of her shipping, shipbuilding, and export industries, was showing a high level of unemployment, accentuated by the low level of her emigration figures. But it may be said with confidence that, in spite of obstructions, the general level of world prosperity was growing with remarkable success in view of the political unrest and bitterness that were the worst legacies of the War, when in 1929 there came a sudden crash, heralded by the collapse in America of the most monstrous fabric of speculation that has ever been seen, and since then the whole system of international exchange of goods has been reduced to a sluggish trickle, owing to some influence which has reduced consumption to a minimum, and left the world helplessly smothered under stocks of goods, so cheap that their prices give their producers no chance of a decent living, and so plentiful that their accumulated stocks are a chronic cause of terror, lest a still further fall in prices should add to the embarrassments of already glutted markets.

Could anything be more absurd than embarrassment due to too great plenty and cheapness of all the goods that we all want to consume? You remember the old story of the man lying dead drunk and the kind old lady saying: 'I'm afraid that poor man is very ill', and the other man, with a chronic thirst, observing: 'Ill is he? I wish I 'ad arf 'is complaint'. Our ancestors who suffered from scarcity and bad harvests, and the Lancashire workers who had no cotton to spin during the American Civil War, would wish, if they came to life again, that they had suffered from half this complaint of too much plenty.

At first sight it seems that this epidemic of plenty and cheapness ought to cause, instead of depression, unemployment, and apprehension, a period of very pleasant enjoyment for consumers—and we are all consumers—enabling them to help themselves at low prices to all the good things that they want. If that were so, the glut would soon be used up and there would be no more fear of a further fall to terrify producers. But, unfortunately, when we go into the shops and markets to supply our daily needs, we find that the fall in prices, so severe in the products of the farm and mine, has only been to a very slight extent reflected in those of the factory; and that by the time the finished article has come through the hands of merchants, dealers, and retailers on to the counters of the shops, the alleged cheapness of everything is largely an illusion. This is one of the root causes of the present depression, because the primary producers, as they are called—those who grow and dig up the raw materials of our food and comforts—get a low price for their crops and output, but have to pay comparatively high ones for clothes, tools, and equipment that they have to buy. So their purchasing power is diminished, to their detriment and that of those who supply their needs.

At the same time most of them are probably indebted to bankers, investors, or other money-lenders, for sums that they have sunk in the development of their enterprise, and have to pay interest on them at a rate which was fixed before the fall in prices. Since their income depends on the prices fetched by their goods, a fall in prices makes this debt charge all the heavier. When wheat loses half its value in the world market, farmers who grow it have to sell twice as much in order to meet the charges of their creditors, and countries such as Canada, Australia, and Argentina, among whose exports wheat is an important item, find it twice as difficult to provide the interest and sinking funds for the loans that they have raised abroad.

With the primary producers thus hard hit and their purchasing power reduced, the manufacturers and merchants and shipowners and railwaymen, and all others who supply their needs, find the outlet for their goods and services diminished, and so business of all kinds slackens, profits are reduced, and unemployment increases. This loss and depression falls in the first instance on employers and shareholders—those who divide the final profit and suffer the loss, in times when losses are prevalent, of production and commerce. But it soon spreads to other classes as the diminished purchasing power of the producers and business men makes itself felt. Lawyers have fewer clients who can afford the luxury of expensive litigation, doctors find that fewer patients have money to spend on ·being ill, parents think twice about sending their children to fashionable schools, newspapers get fewer advertisements and so have less to spend on writers and journalists, and so the disease spreads all through the community, except among those who work for fixed wages or salaries or live on incomes derived from fixed interest securities; and even they are likely to be affected if the evil lasts long enough, for there is less demand for the work of the wage and salary earners, so that, even if they successfully resist reductions, fewer of them are employed, while the rentiers, those who are creditors of governments or of industry, are likely to find that their income is not nearly as secure as it looked when they made the investment.

But what everybody naturally wants to know is why this sudden crisis of over-plenty and over-cheapness happened, and what is to be done to cure it. The explanation that has been most prominently given by high economic authority and most heartily endorsed by business men is, mishandling of the world's money supply by the central banks. Mr. Keynes has accused the central banks of engaging in an 'internecine struggle for gold stocks', and Sir Henry Strakosch has demonstrated with a formidable array of facts and figures how the movement of gold to America and France has depleted the stocks of other countries, and has implied that lack of international co-operation in monetary policy has been the cause of this movement and that it is at the back of the collapse in prices that has caused so much trouble.

This opinion, that gold and its faulty handling is the root of the mischief, is endorsed by Professor Cassel, the distinguished Swedish economist, though he arrives at this conclusion after enumerating, in eloquent terms, a large number of other influences that have tended to warp the course of trade. In an address delivered at the end of May 1931 to the Bankers' Institute in London he tells us that the present generation has been guilty of a whole series of appalling mistakes, faults, and violations of fundamental economic principles—the War itself, the claiming of war debts and reparations without being willing to accept payment in goods, the division of the world's market into watertight compartments, prohibitions of the free movement of men and of capital, preventing, by valorization schemes, the natural adjustment of prices, creating monopolies of enterprise and of labour, developing systems of doles, calculated to increase the immobility of labour and to ruin public finances, and starting radical movements which had destroyed confidence and the spirit of enterprise, on which our whole economic life is founded.

To this impressive list of mistakes Professor Cassel might have added one that is perhaps still more important, namely, the continued cherishing, in spite of the efforts of the League of Nations, of the war spirit in Europe, and an enormous rate of expenditure on armaments. But even the list that he gives seems to show that misuse of the world's gold resources, and the central bankers who are supposed to be responsible for it, can hardly be held to be the sole cause of our troubles. There is, however, some weight in Professor Cassel's contention that all these things fail to explain the present crisis, because in spite of them the world enjoyed, from 1924 to 1929, a period of prosperity and progress. Accordingly, he looked for something that at once altered the situation and produced the crisis, and this something he found in the fall in prices since the middle of 1929. This fall he considered to be a 'monetary phenomenon', and as a remedy he suggested a systematic reduction of central banks' requirements of gold reserves, and proposed the immediate abrogation of all laws by which their gold stocks are regulated.

How such a change would affect the present situation it is difficult to see, in view of the fact that the central banks of America and France, the chief sinners (whether by their own fault or others) in the matter of piling up gold stocks, have already got gold stocks far in excess of legal requirements.

But this prevalent fashion for making gold and central bankers the culprits to be pilloried, as the cause of all the world's evils, reminds one of the habit that was lately common among doctors for ascribing all kinds of bodily ills to the appendix and for immediately removing it from any patient who came within their reach. In those days a man was picked up unconscious in a London street and carried to a hospital where the house surgeon at once diagnosed the case as one of acute appendicitis and proposed to operate immediately. But when the victim was undressed there was found tattooed across that portion of him that was threatened with incision the following legend—'Please do not operate for appendicitis it has been done three times.' The poor man was subject to cataleptic fits, and so had been frequently subjected to the attentions of surgeons with appendicitis on the brain.

In the same way it is important not to let ourselves get gold stocks on the brain or to accuse central bankers of causing accumulations of gold, which may have rolled into their vaults without any encouragement from them. It is very easy to exaggerate the power of central banks to control movements of gold. If the metal is pouring in, it does so because the country has a balance of payments in its favour, because it is selling abroad more goods and services than it is buying and is not investing the balance; but a central bank cannot make the country buy more, or reduce its tariffs, or induce its citizens to invest abroad when they have lost confidence in the solvency of those who want to borrow. All that it can do is to lower its official rate, and so make money cheap with a view to stimulating investment. Money has lately been cheaper in New York than anywhere else, but Americans have shown no inclination to lend abroad because the general mistrust and lack of confidence have made them prefer to keep their money at home.

In fact the mood and temper of the American public, inducing it to act in a way that was directly contrary to the wishes of its banking authorities, have probably been the most important of the many causes of the collapse in prices and in trade. For some years, as has been already recorded, the United States enjoyed an era of unexampled prosperity, which was confidently believed by its inhabitants to have come to stay. One of the accompanying symptoms of this prosperity was a great rise in the prices of American railroad, industrial, and public utility securities, which encouraged its very speculatively minded inhabitants to buy these securities in the expectation of selling them again at a higher level, which they were able to do repeatedly as a fresh stream of buyers continually came forward, seeing certain fortunes to be earned from being, as it was called, 'bulls of the United States'. Instead of being based on the income returned to the buyer by the dividends paid on the shares, prices began to be based on the total earnings of the companies. There was a good deal of reason in this change of principle, but when speculators went further and based prices on the earnings that the companies might be expected to be going to earn in years to come, on the assumption that the prosperity of the United States was certain to continue to grow, the position began to get dangerous. The American banking authorities did their utmost to stop the gamble, but were powerless as long as the temper of the public kept the bit between its teeth. The only weapon in their hand was to make money dear, and that this weapon was of no avail, with prices soaring as they did, was clear from the fact that very high rates—8 and 10 per cent., and on one occasion as much as 20 per cent.—were paid by the New York stock exchange for money wanted for financing this gamble. It did not matter to speculators if they were charged such rates for money to gamble with, as long as the gamble was profitable enough to put clear gains into their pockets after paying all charges.

But when these things happened all the world was affected, because impoverished Europe, which was so badly in need of cash and had so many customers who wanted cash still more, began to send money to America either to take part in the gamble or to earn the high money rates that were paid by those who were engaged in it. And so the international capital market, instead of supplying the needs of backward countries that wanted to borrow in order to supply themselves with equipment, was diverted to the richest country in the world, which wanted not equipment, but funds to be used in the biggest speculation ever seen; and it has already been noted that a steady stream of lending, by the developed countries, to those at an earlier stage, was an essential item in the prosperity of world-trade both in the pre-War period and in the years of its expansion that preceded the collapse. The reversing of this stream and its flow to the country that ought to have been the freest lender, was a hard blow to trade and to the consumption of commodities that was necessary to maintain their prices and absorb the increasing output.

But it was the American public, and those who encouraged it in gambling, that were responsible for this movement, and not the Federal Reserve banks, which did their best to check the speculation. And when the collapse in the New York stock market came, then the profits that the American public had so long been making out of it abruptly ceased and were converted into severe losses that affected every class in the community. The spending power of the Americans was reduced at a blow, and for many kinds of goods the American public is by far the largest consumer. It is true that by means of a very heavy tariff they keep out foreign manufactures as far as possible ; but in normal times their tourists used to flock to Europe and spend there a large part of the surplus that they earned as world-creditor and as a great exporter of cotton, wheat, automobiles, and other articles. With the collapse of the boom much of this business, so pleasant and profitable for all concerned, was stopped. By concentrating on a gamble in her own securities and forgetting that even the richest country cannot afford to ignore the interests of its oversea customers, America inflicted a blow on world-trade which reacted on her own commerce and prosperity with severe effect.

This American collapse came on the top of all the mistakes and follies enumerated by Professor Cassel, and other causes which had hindered the growth of world-trade, such as 'technological' unemployment, due to the mechanization of agriculture and industry, civil war in China, the new régime in Russia, hostile to and resented by the ruling powers in most of the other countries of the world, political unrest in India and South America, and political bitterness in Europe, accentuated by the results of the German general election in the autumn of 1930, when the sweeping success of the Hitler party made France more than ever anxious as to what was going to happen next. It almost seemed that all that had been achieved by the Locarno agreement and the Kellogg pact had been of no avail, and in the autumn of 1930 quite serious people in the business circles of London were discussing apprehensions of war on the Continent in the spring of 1931.

Such fears were, naturally, especially infectious in France, and made her persist in the habits which had led to the immense accumulation of gold by the Bank of France. In this case, as in America's, causes beyond the control of the central bank had brought and continued to bring gold into its vaults. The thrifty French people, according to their ingrained habit, were spending less than they received in the international exchange of goods and services, and, instead of investing their surplus abroad as they had been accustomed to doing before the War, were piling it up on deposit in foreign centres or investing it temporarily in bills of exchange or other short-dated securities. They were not going, owing to the disturbed political atmosphere, to let their money out of their sight. Then there came a time when, owing to rising internal prices and the activity of French home-trade, money was wanted in France, and owing to the somewhat primitive system of the French money market, the commercial banks there could most easily get money, in the form of Bank of France notes, by taking gold to the Bank of France. And so they brought home part of the balances that, as above described, they held in foreign centres, and in default of other means of payment, they brought them home in the form of gold, so accentuating that maldistribution of gold, which has been, as we saw, laid at the door of central banks, but in fact happened owing to the mistrustful temper of the investing public, or of the public which refused to invest.

And so the international capital market, on the free working of which world-trade has been shown to be so much dependent, was more than ever dried up, because gold was sucked away from the centres, of which London was (owing to the domestic pre-occupations of New York) the chief, which might have lent abroad more readily if it had not been for the gold drain that was crippling their financial resources and sapping their confidence. But these matters will be more fittingly discussed when we come to the subject of International Finance. For the present it is clear from what has already been said that economic success was won through international co-operation and the recognition that all the nations, even the richest and most self-sufficient, depend for prosperity on that of all the others; and the failure happened, not because the central banks scrambled for gold, but because America concentrated its energies on a gamble in its own securities, and sucked in money, sorely needed elsewhere, to finance it, and then suffered from a collapse which shattered the buying power of by far the richest market in the world; and because other nations indulged in political vagaries which increased bitterness and apprehension and greatly accentuated the effects of the economic nationalism which had obstructed trade throughout the after-War period.

ASPECTS OF INTERNATIONAL FINANCE

By HARTLEY WITHERS

IT was shown in a previous article how essential to the smooth working of world-trade is the steady progress of the system by which buying power is distributed throughout the nations by means of international loans. In the pre-War period of economic success some £200,000,000 to £300,000,000 used to be lent year by year by the old-established creditor countries of Europe, among which England and France were the chief, with Germany making steady progress as a lender, and the smaller countries—Holland, Belgium, and Scandinavia—making a useful contribution. These sums were placed in the United States, then still on balance a borrower, Canada, India, and the other British Dominions, Russia (which attracted large loans from France), the South American Republics, China, Japan, and other places in the Far East. The money so lent enabled the borrowers to purchase the goods and services furnished by the industrial and manufacturing countries in the form of railway rolling stock, equipment for ports and docks and road-making, agricultural plant and machinery, and so to increase their own productive power and supply food and materials for their own inhabitants and to their oversea customers.

Too often, of course, these foreign loans or part of them were used for less legitimate purposes—balancing of budgets that ought to have been balanced by taxation, or expenditure on armaments, stimulated by nationalistic feeling and propaganda adroitly carried on by firms that lived by supplying weapons of destruction.

On the whole, however, as is shown by the record of the world's economic progress during the century before the War, this system of trade assisted by loans worked wel both for borrowers and lenders. After the War its revival and maintenance were evidently necessary, if trade expansion was to be resumed and if the dislocation left as a war legacy was to be amended. During some years, as has already been recorded, the activity of the international loan market helped the world to revive its trade in spite of new trade barriers and other difficulties. England's power to lend abroad had been restricted by high taxation and domestic capital needs, and France was for some years embarrassed by currency depreciation, and when the franc had been stabilized was unwilling, owing to political apprehensions, to take her old place as a long-term lender. Germany, instead of having funds available to place abroad, was struggling first with an incredibly depreciated mark, and then, after the Dawes and Young Plans had been devised by her creditors, with the need to pay Reparations, which for some time she effected by means of money advanced to her. But these gaps in the market were filled by the United States which, being owed money by all the world and being at the same time most anxious to develop her export trade and most unwilling to admit foreign goods over her stiff tariff barrier, was, during the years of general prosperity up to 1928, a free lender of capital abroad. Then, as has been shown, she concentrated her attention on the prospects of her own securities and drew in money from other countries to finance her great gamble in them. At the same time England's power to lend abroad was diminished by pre-occupations concerning the maintenance of the exchange value of the pound sterling and by industrial difficulties which made her cost of production high and made her less able to compete with countries that had lower taxation, lower wages, and generally lower standards of living. France maintained her policy of preferring to lend abroad only on such terms as enabled her to recall the money on demand. And so the international capital market, severely cut down during 1929, and supplied rather more freely (owing to the spell of cheap money that followed the collapse of the American boom) during 1930, practically dried up during 1931.

Under this blow, world trade went to pieces and with it the prices of wholesale commodities. The position of the debtor countries was thus made doubly difficult. At the very moment when the borrowing facilities on which they had been accustomed to rely had been withdrawn, they found that the commodities which they had to sell abroad, in order to cover the service of their debts and pay for the goods that they needed to import, had fallen so much in value that they had to choose between default or serious curtailment of their imports. In so far as they chose the latter course—and they all had to do so to a certain extent —their action reduced the profits and activity of the industries of the creditor countries, increased unemployment there and generally quickened the spin of the vicious circle in which world trade was whirling. And so the miserable spectacle was produced—so discreditable to all who have lately been responsible for the management of the world's affairs—of a crisis threatening many countries with bankruptcy, and inflicting distress upon all, owing to too great a supply of goods which were offered so cheap that it did not pay to produce them, and yet were unable to find buyers because something had gone wrong with the system of marketing and consumption.

From this deplorable state of things one or two obvious conclusions can be drawn. In the first place, it is directly traceable to the effects of the War, which thrust an immense heap of wealth into the hands of America, and gave her a position in world economy which she has not yet learnt to fill with a due sense of responsibility; it also first crippled France and then left her so apprehensive that she has been unable to resume her old eminence as a provider of capital for other nations; and finally, it left Reparation and war-debt payments to warp the course of trade and reduce the buying power of those who have to pay them. So that if we want to avoid this sort of tragical absurdity in the future, there is one obvious thing that we can all do, and that is, support by every possible effort the work of the League of Nations. A second conclusion is, that the consequences of the collapse of world trade and the insolvency that it threatens to inflict on so many debtors, with the accompaniment of losses to creditors, are so serious that they have been an eloquent lesson in favour of co-operation—a lesson that, as we shall see, has not been without practical results.

For the collapse in trade and prices had, as was inevitable, effects which made the trouble still worse. Among the debtors who found it more difficult, owing to the fall in prices and the slackened demand for all kinds of commodities, to meet the charges for which they were liable, Germany's position was in some ways the most difficult because she had, before the collapse, met her Reparation obligation largely by borrowing in that international money market which had been practically closed by the collapse. Moreover, the charge was one that was resented very bitterly by her population, owing to the stupidity with which the victorious Powers had stated in the terms of the Versailles Treaty that it was imposed as a punishment for Germany's war guilt, with the implication that Germany and her allies had been solely responsible for the War. If Reparations had been demanded on the ground that they are a charge that a conquered nation has to pay as a matter of course, and that had been imposed on France by Germany in 1871, the feelings of Germans on the subject would not have been exacerbated by what they describe as the 'war guilt lie'.

As it was, resentment on this point and the growing difficulty of meeting the charge owing to the trade depression added fuel to the flame of German discontent which blazed, in the autumn of 1930, into a surprising result of a general election, which gave an astonishing accession of strength to the 'Hitler' party, which was believed to stand for reaction in favour of autocracy, militarism, and the repudiation of the Reparations obligation. This political symptom alarmed both the Germans themselves and Germany's foreign creditors. It caused the former to start what is called a flight from the mark—that is, it undermined their confidence in the political and financial stability of their own country, and so caused them to dispose of any securities and other assets that they could sell abroad and leave the proceeds in foreign currencies in foreign centres; while at the same time the foreign creditors were carrying out the same process by withdrawing from Germany any funds that they had placed there on terms that gave them the power to take them back at call or short notice.

There was thus a double run on Germany, by her own citizens and by her foreign creditors, of whom France and America were the chief. Thus Germany was not only cut off from the facilities that had been afforded by the international capital market, but was called on, at a time when it was difficult to dispose either of securities or of commodities, to repay a large part of the short advances that had been placed with her. Owing to the cessation of long-term lending, she had borrowed extensively from lenders who wished to place their funds at call, and was thus severely embarrassed when they began to want to have their money back.

These troubles were accentuated in the spring of 1931, when it was suddenly discovered that the Credit-Anstalt, an Austrian institution that had most of Austria's banking business in its hands, was in such serious difficulties that external help was immediately required. Austria, a trunkless head shorn of its limbs by the Treaty of Versailles, had suffered severely from the world depression, and its chief bank was, according to Continental methods, deeply involved in its industries. Co-operation in the world of finance is much more easy to secure than in that of politics, and when this Austrian trouble developed, assistance was promptly rendered by the Bank for International Settlements, backed by no less than ten of the leading central banks.

But the Austrian trouble had revealed certain difficulties and started others. French co-operation had been hard to secure, and at one moment when something had to be done quickly, and France was trying to make assistance depend on political conditions, the Bank of England had to make an advance of £4 millions without waiting for the end of the discussion. What was still more important, the run on Germany that had been begun at the time of the Hitler election was quickened by this revelation of weakness in Austria, partly, it was said, because some of Germany's American creditors did not understand that Germany and Austria are different nations, but chiefly, of course, because of the close connexion between the business and financial organizations of the two countries.

At the same time, the German Government was making stupendous efforts, in the face of its internal political difficulties, to meet its embarrassments by drastic economies. On June 6, 1931, it published a manifesto, which was described by the Berlin correspondent of *The Times* as being regarded there as an intimation to the world at large that Germany considered herself to have reached the end of her tether, unless the external pressure upon her was in some way eased. This pronouncement stated that the expenditure of the Reich had been cut down by £75 millions, that Germany had made every effort to fulfil the obligations resulting from a lost war, that she had made, for this purpose, extensive use of foreign assistance, which it was no longer possible to secure, that the limits of the privations which she could inflict on her citizens had been reached, that the economic and financial situation of the

Reich, seriously menaced, inevitably compelled the relief of Germany from the intolerable Reparations obligation, and that the economic recovery of the world was at stake.

A week later the Reichsbank raised its official rate from 5 to 7 per cent., but this movement had little, if any, effect in stopping the run. When a debtor is known to be in difficulties, he is apt merely to increase the apprehensions of his creditors by offering a higher price for accommodation. Dr. Luther, the President of the Reichsbank, explained the necessity for the movement by saying that there had been large withdrawals of credit and sales of securities by foreigners, due not to any economic changes in Germany but to 'occurrences of another kind', referring to the troubles of the Credit-Anstalt and, presumably, the political difficulties which had threatened the maintenance of Dr. Brüning's Government. There had also been, according to *The Times* correspondent, a renewal of the German flight from the mark, while foreign withdrawals were said to have been carried out chiefly by American creditors; France, which had been chiefly blamed for the withdrawals of the previous autumn, was less imperative in her demands in June, probably because most of the French money that had been lent at short notice in Germany had by that time been removed. In the first two weeks of the month the total withdrawals were estimated to have amounted to £40 millions.

It is important to note that this run on Germany was thus due to apprehensions chiefly political in origin, and that the lack of confidence of Germans in their own country was partly responsible for it. If it had not been for this lack of confidence, domestic and foreign, Germany might, apparently, have met her financial liabilities without undue strain.

As it was, the strain was such that it had serious effects on those American banks and institutions that had placed funds in Germany, so much so that President Hoover, who was touring at this time in the Western States, was deeply impressed by the repercussions, actual and possible, of events in Central Europe on the financial position in his own country, seriously weakened by the results of the speculative collapse there followed by acute business depression. On June 20, he made his momentous proposal for a year's suspension of all payments, both of interest and principal, on inter-Governmental debts. In other words, he proposed that all payments on account of Reparations should cease for a year, and that at the same time all payments on account of war debts between the Allied Governments should also be suspended.

When we remember that hitherto the American Administration had steadily discouraged any attempts to raise the question of the revision of war debts, and that the United States Treasury was known to be faced with an enormous deficit on the financial year then ending—it actually turned out, at the end of June, that there had been a gap of £180 millions between revenue and expenditure—it was a highly courageous act on the part of Mr. Hoover to make a proposal which involved a complete reversal of policy and cost the American taxpayer about £50 millions, at a time when the country's finances were so badly disordered.

His bold proposal was received with general approval in America, and produced, for the moment, a complete change of atmosphere in business circles, with a sharp recovery in the prices of securities and commodities. This effort in favour of unity was recognized as so obviously the right remedy for the world's disease, that every one was ready to believe that the patient was on the way to recovery.

But promptitude in acceptance and administration was essential, if the prescription was to act, and was only forthcoming from England and Italy. England accepted the proposal not only with regard to inter-ally debts but also in respect of inter-Imperial and after-War relief obligations, thus inflicting a loss of about £11 millions on her Treasury, already impoverished by extravagance and sluggish revenue. But France hesitated and asked questions, and this hesitation, owing to the long delay that ensued before France was able to accord a guarded and cautious acceptance of the Hoover plan, sufficed to rob it of all its efficiency as an immediate remedy for the evils that were besetting Europe.

Hesitation on the part of France, however, was most natural and reasonable. She was suffering much less than America or England owing to the world depression. She had got most of her money out of Germany, and so stood to lose less by a German collapse. She was asked, under the Hoover Plan, to suffer a loss of nearly £20 millions of revenue in order to secure a breathing space for a neighbour whom she had good reason to regard as formidable, and who had lately, by an Austro-German customs union proposal suddenly sprung on Europe, by a Stahlhelm demonstration and a pocket-battleship, shown no consideration for the susceptibilities of the nation that was now asked to help her round the corner at a considerable sacrifice. Small wonder that France thought it highly necessary to ensure, if possible, that the suspension of Reparations should not be used by Germany for purposes that might be inconvenient to her.

In the meantime, while France was thus naturally hesitating, the run on Germany continued, and did not cease even after France's guarded consent had been given on July 6. In the week that followed, matters were rapidly coming to a head, and a novel feature in international crises was seen in the literally flying visits paid by Dr. Luther, the President of the Reichsbank, first to London and then to Basel to attend a meeting of the International Bank for Settlements, and by the constant telephone talks that were proceeding between New York, London, Paris, and Berlin.

This meeting of the Bank for International Settlements was held on July 13, and on that day the Darmstadter and National Bank, one of the principal German banks, did not open its doors, and the mark was for a short time quoted at 31 to the pound, and a general closing of German banks on the next two days was announced by Presidential decree. At the Basel meeting of the Bank for International Settlements it was found impossible to grant to Germany the assistance, in the shape of a long-term loan, that she required in order to restore confidence in her position. After a session of over twelve hours the Board decided that it was prepared to collaborate in any measures of assistance to Germany that might be secured by the Governments that had been appealed to, and that in the meantime it was prepared to renew a temporary credit of £20 millions, granted to Germany by it, the Federal Reserve Board of the United States, the Bank of France, and the Bank of England.

Thus the problem of restoring confidence in Germany was handed by the international bankers to the Governments, showing that in their opinion the matter was so largely political that only political measures could deal with it.

And so there was a hastily summoned London Conference of world statesmen which sat for three days— July 20 to 23—and finally handed the problem back to the bankers, suggesting that they should take concerted measures for the maintenance, by each of the countries concerned, of the then outstanding volume of credit granted by it to Germany.

Somehow or other, this extremely difficult arrangement was carried out, and by means of this and other measures, it was made possible to resume business in Germany on more or less normal lines. But it was plainly intimated by the bankers to the Governments that the political atmosphere had to be materially improved before financial restoration could be hoped for. A bankers' committee, set up at the suggestion of the London Conference to inquire into the further credit needs of Germany and to study the question of converting her short-term into long-term credits, reported on August 19 in terms which plainly told the Governments that the real solution of the financial problem lay in their hands.

'We think it essential', said this report, 'that before the period of prolongation of credits recommended by the London Conference comes to an end, they (the Governments) should give the world the assurance that international political relations are established on a basis of mutual confidence which is the *sine qua non* of economic recovery.'

Mutual confidence and the co-operation that creates and is created by it are the object for which the League of Nations is always working, and this international crisis is distinguished from those that have preceded it by the influence of the League, and by the good work that it has done in accustoming the nations to regard one another as bodies with which it is not only possible but advantageous to deal on terms of mutual consideration and goodwill. The result of these efforts has been reinforced by the pressure of extreme danger, which was so clearly revealed by the condition into which Germany was being hurried by the action of shortsighted people acting under the influence of political panic.

Germany's position was thus temporarily patched up, pending the recovery of confidence necessary to the flotation of that long-term international loan, to rescue her from dependence on short-term advances, the danger of which, in times of political apprehension, has been shown so clearly. Towards that recovery of confidence, Germany has done much by internal economies and by a plébiscite taken in Prussia, the effect of which was to strengthen the hands of the Government. The more difficult problem of the relations of France and Germany awaits solution, but it should be assisted by the influence of the League of Nations, quickened by that of the sharp lesson lately administered by the experience that Europe has had of the financial consequences of nationalistic exuberances.

But the German crisis had very serious after-effects for England. London, as everyone knows, does an important business as international banker, accepting deposits from other countries and making advances by acceptance and otherwise. When it began to be clear that money lent to Germany was, for the time being, an irrecoverable asset, French and other Continental bankers who had lent money to London began to be apprehensive as to London's power to repay them, owing to the lock-up of English money in Germany. And so the run on Germany led to a run on London, and the withdrawal from the Bank of England of £32 millions in gold during the last two weeks of July 1931. The Bank of England still had a gold stock of £134 millions, but thought it advisable to procure outside assistance, which was readily granted by the Bank of France and the Federal Reserve bank of New York, in the form of a credit of £25 millions from each of them, in their respective currencies.

That the Bank of England had to have recourse to outside assistance was a not unprecedented event, and was due on this occasion to the state of panic that prevailed on the Continent, where banks of all countries had been hit by the industrial depression and were also being pressed by their customers for money which the latter were taking away and hoarding. Recollections of the after-War inflation were still strong in the minds of all and doubtless helped to stimulate the hoarding habit and the demand for American dollars first in Germany and then in other Continental countries. In other words, Europe had for the time being gone back to barbarism in banking matters, and banking requires a civilized community to work for if it is to perform its functions properly. No bank can stand, without outside assistance, a run that is persistent enough ; and in the state of nerves then prevalent on the Continent no one could say how long and how far the demands on London's gold stock would go on.

As it was, it was increased and prolonged by a domestic political event, namely the publication, just at the end of July, of the report of a Committee appointed to consider the question of national expenditure. It stated that when the next budget had to be met it would show a deficit of £120 millions, unless in the meantime expenditure was drastically curtailed. Since the expenditure programme included £52 millions for debt redemption, the figure was not nearly as alarming as it looked, but the report produced a storm of criticism, accusing the Government of having brought the country to the verge of bankruptcy, and also of having caused the run on London by its reckless extravagance.

These criticisms were as grossly overstated, as is usual when political controversy is embittered. The country was nowhere near to bankruptcy, and an unbalanced budget was a matter that was well within its power to deal with as soon as it meant to do so. Moreover, America was faced with a much bigger deficit actually realized, but there was no run on New York, and it has been shown how the run on London had grown out of the run on Germany and had little to do with English politics, though the methods of Socialist finance here had certainly caused a certain amount of flight from the pound, both domestic and foreign.

But of course England's foreign creditors, when they heard these prophecies of her imminent ruin, took them at their face value and continued the run ; and further assistance was evidently difficult to get without the promise of economies that would restore confidence.

London still had over £130 millions of gold ; and it is possible that if she had calmly announced that she meant to let her gold go if necessary and revalue the pound at a lower level, she would either have obliged her foreign creditors, in their own interests, to hold the pound up for her, or she would have greatly lightened her industrial difficulties by making this fresh start, with the pound stabilized at a new level. But such measures would have needed an iron nerve to carry them out, and would have involved very serious dangers. What was done was, that the foreign bankers were given some reassurance about British finance by the establishment of a National Government pledged to balance the budget, and New York and Paris were then ready to oblige again with further credits of £80 millions, to be granted to the British Government.

Summing up the lessons of this miserable story, it is clear that international banking, by its extensive use of short-term credits, has laid any country open to attack, by the withdrawal of such credits, if it rouses apprehensions or misunderstandings by political actions or utterances. The run on Germany was started by the Hitler election. The run on London, originally due to the *sequelae* of the German crisis, was made so serious by political clamour in England that it obliged the British Government to borrow abroad a large sum that it did not need except for the purpose of saving the pound from depreciation. It may thus be claimed that international finance, always a steadying influence in international politics, and far better aware of the need for co-operation among the nations than the statesmen who steer the political ship, has lately given the world a useful lesson on the consequences of disunity.

BOOKS FOR REFERENCE

R. G. Hawtrey. *The Gold Standard in Theory and Practice.* Longmans, Green.

Dr. Robert Eisler. *This Money Maze.* Search Publishing Co.

Lord Melchett. *Why the Crisis?* Gollancz.

H. Withers. *Everybody's Business.* Cape.